BIRDS & BLOOMS

daily planner 2013

ONCE UPON A TIME, Hans Christian Andersen penned these wise words: "Just living is not enough…one must have sunshine, freedom and a little flower." Being close to nature certainly makes for a more fulfilled life, but these days, who has time to stop and smell the roses?

That's where the *Birds & Blooms Daily Planner* comes in handy. Our daily date book, at-a-glance calendars and special-event list help you organize your life so you can spend more time enjoying the people and activities you love most.

Now, when you're on the go, you can take Mother Nature along. Every week, we share top tips and insider facts on your favorite birds, plants and butterflies, each accompanied by a beautiful photo—many from birders and gardeners just like you! A *Birds & Blooms* planner wouldn't be complete without tools to keep your birding and gardening talents on track. You're sure to turn to our useful guides, charts and checklists time and again. Flip to page 174 to get started.

This year, savor nature's beauty wherever you are, and you'll be well on your way to living life to its fullest.

Enjoy!

Stacy Tornio

Stacy Tornio
Editor, *Birds & Blooms*

This planner belongs to:

_____
NAME

_____
ADDRESS

_____

_____

_____
PHONE

_____

EDITORIAL
EDITOR-IN-CHIEF Catherine Cassidy

EXECUTIVE EDITOR/PRINT & DIGITAL BOOKS Stephen C. George
CREATIVE DIRECTOR Howard Greenberg
EDITORIAL SERVICES MANAGER Kerri Balliet

SENIOR EDITOR/PRINT & DIGITAL BOOKS Mark Hagen
ASSOCIATE EDITOR Ellie Martin Cliffe
ASSOCIATE CREATIVE DIRECTOR Edwin Robles Jr.
ART DIRECTOR Raeann Sundholm
CONTENT PRODUCTION MANAGER Julie Wagner
LAYOUT DESIGNER Catherine Fletcher
COPY CHIEF Deb Warlaumont Mulvey
COPY EDITOR Alysse Gear
ASSISTANT PHOTO COORDINATOR Mary Ann Koebernik
EDITORIAL ASSISTANT Marilyn Iczkowski

EXECUTIVE EDITOR Heather Lamb
CREATIVE DIRECTOR Sharon K. Nelson
EDITOR, *BIRDS & BLOOMS* Stacy Tornio
ART DIRECTOR, *BIRDS & BLOOMS* Sue Myers

BUSINESS
VICE PRESIDENT, PUBLISHER Russell S. Ellis
ASSOCIATE PUBLISHER Chris Dolan
NEW YORK Greg Messina, John Dyckman, Sabrina Ng,
Megan Opperman, nysales@rd.com
CHICAGO Monica Thomas Kamradt, nysales@rd.com
WEST COAST Catherine Marcussen, nysales@rd.com
CLASSIFIEDS M.I. Integrated Media, Alycia Isabelle, brenda@mi-ms.com

CORPORATE INTEGRATED SALES DIRECTOR Steve Sottile
VP, DIGITAL SALES AND DEVELOPMENT Dan Meehan
DIGITAL/INTEGRATED DIRECTOR Kelly Paxson

EXECUTIVE DIRECTOR, BRAND MARKETING Leah West
VP, CREATIVE DIRECTOR Paul Livornese
MARKETING MANAGER Katie Gaon Wilson
ASSOCIATE MARKETING MANAGER Emily Moore

VP, MAGAZINE MARKETING Dave Fiegel

READER'S DIGEST NORTH AMERICA
PRESIDENT Dan Lagani

PRESIDENT, CANADA Tony Cioffi
PRESIDENT, BOOKS AND HOME ENTERTAINING Harold Clarke
CHIEF FINANCIAL OFFICER Howard Halligan
**VICE PRESIDENT, GENERAL MANAGER,
READER'S DIGEST MEDIA** Marilynn Jacobs
CHIEF MARKETING OFFICER Renee Jordan
VICE PRESIDENT, CHIEF SALES OFFICER Mark Josephson
**VICE PRESIDENT, GENERAL MANAGER,
RD MILWAUKEE** Lisa Karpinski
VICE PRESIDENT, CHIEF STRATEGY OFFICER
Jacqueline Majers Lachman
VICE PRESIDENT, MARKETING & CREATIVE SERVICES
Elizabeth Tighe
VICE PRESIDENT, CHIEF CONTENT OFFICER Liz Vaccariello

THE READER'S DIGEST ASSOCIATION, INC.
PRESIDENT AND CHIEF EXECUTIVE OFFICER Robert E. Guth

©2012 Reiman Media Group, LLC
5400 S. 60th St., Greendale WI 53129

International Standard Book Number (10): 1-61765-042-0
International Standard Book Number (13): 978-1-61765-042-0

Printed in China
1 3 5 7 9 10 8 6 4 2

BIRDSANDBLOOMS.COM

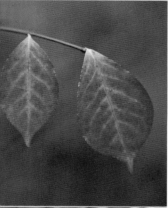

HUMMINGBIRD: COUNTRY PHOTOS BY LORI NAANES; LEAVES: COMSTOCK / GETTY IMAGES; SWALLOWTAIL: HOWARD CHEEK

Table of Contents

2013 Calendar and Holidays

JANUARY 2013

S	M	T	W	T	F	S
		1	2	3	4	5
6	7	8	9	10	11	12
13	14	15	16	17	18	19
20	21	22	23	24	25	26
27	28	29	30	31		

1 New Year's Day
6 Epiphany
21 Martin Luther King Jr. Day

FEBRUARY 2013

S	M	T	W	T	F	S
					1	2
3	4	5	6	7	8	9
10	11	12	13	14	15	16
17	18	19	20	21	22	23
24	25	26	27	28		

2 Groundhog Day
12 Lincoln's Birthday
13 Ash Wednesday
14 Valentine's Day
18 Presidents Day
22 Washington's Birthday

MAY 2013

S	M	T	W	T	F	S
			1	2	3	4
5	6	7	8	9	10	11
12	13	14	15	16	17	18
19	20	21	22	23	24	25
26	27	28	29	30	31	

1 May Day
5 Cinco de Mayo
12 Mother's Day
18 Armed Forces Day
20 Victoria Day (Canada)
27 Memorial Day

JUNE 2013

S	M	T	W	T	F	S
						1
2	3	4	5	6	7	8
9	10	11	12	13	14	15
16	17	18	19	20	21	22
23	24	25	26	27	28	29
30						

9 Children's Sunday
14 Flag Day
16 Father's Day
21 Summer begins
24 St. Jean Baptiste Day (Canada)

SEPTEMBER 2013

S	M	T	W	T	F	S
1	2	3	4	5	6	7
8	9	10	11	12	13	14
15	16	17	18	19	20	21
22	23	24	25	26	27	28
29	30					

2 Labor Day
4 Rosh Hashanah begins
8 National Grandparents' Day
11 Patriot Day
13 Yom Kippur begins
22 Autumn begins
28 National Good Neighbor Day

OCTOBER 2013

S	M	T	W	T	F	S
		1	2	3	4	5
6	7	8	9	10	11	12
13	14	15	16	17	18	19
20	21	22	23	24	25	26
27	28	29	30	31		

14 Columbus Day
14 Thanksgiving Day (Canada)
19 Sweetest Day
31 Halloween

MARCH 2013

S	M	T	W	T	F	S
					1	2
3	4	5	6	7	8	9
10	11	12	13	14	15	16
17	18	19	20	21	22	23
24	25	26	27	28	29	30
31						

10 Daylight Saving Time begins
17 St. Patrick's Day
20 Spring begins
24 Palm Sunday
25 Passover begins
29 Good Friday
31 Easter

APRIL 2013

S	M	T	W	T	F	S
	1	2	3	4	5	6
7	8	9	10	11	12	13
14	15	16	17	18	19	20
21	22	23	24	25	26	27
28	29	30				

1 April Fools' Day
13 Jefferson's Birthday
15 Income Tax Day
26 Arbor Day

JULY 2013

S	M	T	W	T	F	S
	1	2	3	4	5	6
7	8	9	10	11	12	13
14	15	16	17	18	19	20
21	22	23	24	25	26	27
28	29	30	31			

1 Canada Day (Canada)
4 Independence Day

AUGUST 2013

S	M	T	W	T	F	S
				1	2	3
4	5	6	7	8	9	10
11	12	13	14	15	16	17
18	19	20	21	22	23	24
25	26	27	28	29	30	31

5 Civic Holiday (Canada)

NOVEMBER 2013

S	M	T	W	T	F	S
					1	2
3	4	5	6	7	8	9
10	11	12	13	14	15	16
17	18	19	20	21	22	23
24	25	26	27	28	29	30

3 Daylight Saving Time ends
5 Election Day
11 Veterans Day
11 Remembrance Day (Canada)
27 Hanukkah begins
28 Thanksgiving Day

DECEMBER 2013

S	M	T	W	T	F	S
1	2	3	4	5	6	7
8	9	10	11	12	13	14
15	16	17	18	19	20	21
22	23	24	25	26	27	28
29	30	31				

6 St. Nicholas' Day
21 Winter begins
24 Christmas Eve
25 Christmas Day
26 Boxing Day (Canada)
31 New Year's Eve

2012 Calendar and Holidays

JANUARY 2012

S	M	T	W	T	F	S
1	2	3	4	5	6	7
8	9	10	11	12	13	14
15	16	17	18	19	20	21
22	23	24	25	26	27	28
29	30	31				

1 New Year's Day
6 Epiphany
16 Martin Luther King Jr. Day

FEBRUARY 2012

S	M	T	W	T	F	S
			1	2	3	4
5	6	7	8	9	10	11
12	13	14	15	16	17	18
19	20	21	22	23	24	25
26	27	28	29			

2 Groundhog Day
12 Lincoln's Birthday
14 Valentine's Day
20 Presidents Day
22 Ash Wednesday
22 Washington's Birthday

MARCH 2012

S	M	T	W	T	F	S
				1	2	3
4	5	6	7	8	9	10
11	12	13	14	15	16	17
18	19	20	21	22	23	24
25	26	27	28	29	30	31

11 Daylight Saving Time begins
17 St. Patrick's Day
20 Spring begins

APRIL 2012

S	M	T	W	T	F	S
1	2	3	4	5	6	7
8	9	10	11	12	13	14
15	16	17	18	19	20	21
22	23	24	25	26	27	28
29	30					

1 April Fools' Day
1 Palm Sunday
6 Good Friday
6 Passover begins
8 Easter
13 Jefferson's Birthday
17 Income Tax Day
27 Arbor Day

MAY 2012

S	M	T	W	T	F	S
		1	2	3	4	5
6	7	8	9	10	11	12
13	14	15	16	17	18	19
20	21	22	23	24	25	26
27	28	29	30	31		

1 May Day
5 Cinco de Mayo
13 Mother's Day
19 Armed Forces Day
21 Victoria Day (Canada)
28 Memorial Day

JUNE 2012

S	M	T	W	T	F	S
					1	2
3	4	5	6	7	8	9
10	11	12	13	14	15	16
17	18	19	20	21	22	23
24	25	26	27	28	29	30

10 Children's Sunday
14 Flag Day
17 Father's Day
20 Summer begins
24 St. Jean Baptiste Day (Canada)

JULY 2012

S	M	T	W	T	F	S
1	2	3	4	5	6	7
8	9	10	11	12	13	14
15	16	17	18	19	20	21
22	23	24	25	26	27	28
29	30	31				

1 Canada Day (Canada)
4 Independence Day

AUGUST 2012

S	M	T	W	T	F	S
			1	2	3	4
5	6	7	8	9	10	11
12	13	14	15	16	17	18
19	20	21	22	23	24	25
26	27	28	29	30	31	

6 Civic Holiday (Canada)

SEPTEMBER 2012

S	M	T	W	T	F	S
						1
2	3	4	5	6	7	8
9	10	11	12	13	14	15
16	17	18	19	20	21	22
23	24	25	26	27	28	29
30						

3 Labor Day
9 National Grandparents' Day
11 Patriot Day
16 Rosh Hashanah begins
22 Autumn begins
25 Yom Kippur begins
28 National Good Neighbor Day

OCTOBER 2012

S	M	T	W	T	F	S
	1	2	3	4	5	6
7	8	9	10	11	12	13
14	15	16	17	18	19	20
21	22	23	24	25	26	27
28	29	30	31			

8 Columbus Day
8 Thanksgiving Day (Canada)
20 Sweetest Day
31 Halloween

NOVEMBER 2012

S	M	T	W	T	F	S
				1	2	3
4	5	6	7	8	9	10
11	12	13	14	15	16	17
18	19	20	21	22	23	24
25	26	27	28	29	30	

4 Daylight Saving Time ends
6 Election Day
11 Veterans Day
11 Remembrance Day (Canada)
22 Thanksgiving Day

DECEMBER 2012

S	M	T	W	T	F	S
						1
2	3	4	5	6	7	8
9	10	11	12	13	14	15
16	17	18	19	20	21	22
23	24	25	26	27	28	29
30	31					

6 St. Nicholas' Day
8 Hanukkah begins
21 Winter begins
24 Christmas Eve
25 Christmas Day
26 Boxing Day (Canada)
31 New Year's Eve

2014 Calendar and Holidays

JANUARY 2014

S	M	T	W	T	F	S
			1	2	3	4
5	6	7	8	9	10	11
12	13	14	15	16	17	18
19	20	21	22	23	24	25
26	27	28	29	30	31	

1 New Year's Day
6 Epiphany
20 Martin Luther King Jr. Day

FEBRUARY 2014

S	M	T	W	T	F	S
						1
2	3	4	5	6	7	8
9	10	11	12	13	14	15
16	17	18	19	20	21	22
23	24	25	26	27	28	

2 Groundhog Day
12 Lincoln's Birthday
14 Valentine's Day
17 Presidents Day
22 Washington's Birthday

MARCH 2014

S	M	T	W	T	F	S
						1
2	3	4	5	6	7	8
9	10	11	12	13	14	15
16	17	18	19	20	21	22
23	24	25	26	27	28	29
30	31					

5 Ash Wednesday
9 Daylight Saving Time begins
17 St. Patrick's Day
20 Spring begins

APRIL 2014

S	M	T	W	T	F	S
		1	2	3	4	5
6	7	8	9	10	11	12
13	14	15	16	17	18	19
20	21	22	23	24	25	26
27	28	29	30			

1 April Fools' Day
13 Palm Sunday
13 Jefferson's Birthday
14 Passover begins
15 Income Tax Day
18 Good Friday
20 Easter
25 Arbor Day

MAY 2014

S	M	T	W	T	F	S
				1	2	3
4	5	6	7	8	9	10
11	12	13	14	15	16	17
18	19	20	21	22	23	24
25	26	27	28	29	30	31

1 May Day
5 Cinco de Mayo
11 Mother's Day
17 Armed Forces Day
19 Victoria Day (Canada)
26 Memorial Day

JUNE 2014

S	M	T	W	T	F	S
1	2	3	4	5	6	7
8	9	10	11	12	13	14
15	16	17	18	19	20	21
22	23	24	25	26	27	28
29	30					

8 Children's Sunday
14 Flag Day
15 Father's Day
21 Summer begins
24 St. Jean Baptiste Day (Canada)

JULY 2014

S	M	T	W	T	F	S
		1	2	3	4	5
6	7	8	9	10	11	12
13	14	15	16	17	18	19
20	21	22	23	24	25	26
27	28	29	30	31		

1 Canada Day
4 Independence Day

AUGUST 2014

S	M	T	W	T	F	S
					1	2
3	4	5	6	7	8	9
10	11	12	13	14	15	16
17	18	19	20	21	22	23
24	25	26	27	28	29	30
31						

4 Civic Holiday (Canada)

SEPTEMBER 2014

S	M	T	W	T	F	S
	1	2	3	4	5	6
7	8	9	10	11	12	13
14	15	16	17	18	19	20
21	22	23	24	25	26	27
28	29	30				

1 Labor Day
7 National Grandparents' Day
11 Patriot Day
23 Autumn begins
24 Rosh Hashanah begins
28 National Good Neighbor Day

OCTOBER 2014

S	M	T	W	T	F	S
			1	2	3	4
5	6	7	8	9	10	11
12	13	14	15	16	17	18
19	20	21	22	23	24	25
26	27	28	29	30	31	

3 Yom Kippur begins
13 Columbus Day
13 Thanksgiving Day (Canada)
18 Sweetest Day
31 Halloween

NOVEMBER 2014

S	M	T	W	T	F	S
						1
2	3	4	5	6	7	8
9	10	11	12	13	14	15
16	17	18	19	20	21	22
23	24	25	26	27	28	29
30						

2 Daylight Saving Time ends
4 Election Day
11 Veterans Day
11 Remembrance Day (Canada)
27 Thanksgiving Day

DECEMBER 2014

S	M	T	W	T	F	S
	1	2	3	4	5	6
7	8	9	10	11	12	13
14	15	16	17	18	19	20
21	22	23	24	25	26	27
28	29	30	31			

6 St. Nicholas' Day
16 Hanukkah begins
21 Winter begins
24 Christmas Eve
25 Christmas Day
26 Boxing Day (Canada)
31 New Year's Eve

2015 Calendar and Holidays

JANUARY 2015

S	M	T	W	T	F	S
				1	2	3
4	5	6	7	8	9	10
11	12	13	14	15	16	17
18	19	20	21	22	23	24
25	26	27	28	29	30	31

1 New Year's Day
6 Epiphany
19 Martin Luther King Jr. Day

FEBRUARY 2015

S	M	T	W	T	F	S
1	2	3	4	5	6	7
8	9	10	11	12	13	14
15	16	17	18	19	20	21
22	23	24	25	26	27	28

2 Groundhog Day
12 Lincoln's Birthday
14 Valentine's Day
16 Presidents Day
18 Ash Wednesday
22 Washington's Birthday

MARCH 2015

S	M	T	W	T	F	S
1	2	3	4	5	6	7
8	9	10	11	12	13	14
15	16	17	18	19	20	21
22	23	24	25	26	27	28
29	30	31				

7 Daylight Saving Time begins
17 St. Patrick's Day
20 Spring begins
29 Palm Sunday

APRIL 2015

S	M	T	W	T	F	S
			1	2	3	4
5	6	7	8	9	10	11
12	13	14	15	16	17	18
19	20	21	22	23	24	25
26	27	28	29	30		

1 April Fools' Day
3 Good Friday
4 Passover begins
5 Easter
13 Jefferson's Birthday
15 Income Tax Day
24 Arbor Day

MAY 2015

S	M	T	W	T	F	S
					1	2
3	4	5	6	7	8	9
10	11	12	13	14	15	16
17	18	19	20	21	22	23
24	25	26	27	28	29	30
31						

1 May Day
5 Cinco de Mayo
10 Mother's Day
16 Armed Forces Day
18 Victoria Day (Canada)
25 Memorial Day

JUNE 2015

S	M	T	W	T	F	S
	1	2	3	4	5	6
7	8	9	10	11	12	13
14	15	16	17	18	19	20
21	22	23	24	25	26	27
28	29	30				

14 Children's Sunday
14 Flag Day
21 Father's Day
21 Summer begins
24 St. Jean Baptiste Day (Canada)

JULY 2015

S	M	T	W	T	F	S
			1	2	3	4
5	6	7	8	9	10	11
12	13	14	15	16	17	18
19	20	21	22	23	24	25
26	27	28	29	30	31	

1 Canada Day (Canada)
4 Independence Day

AUGUST 2015

S	M	T	W	T	F	S
						1
2	3	4	5	6	7	8
9	10	11	12	13	14	15
16	17	18	19	20	21	22
23	24	25	26	27	28	29
30	31					

3 Civic Holiday (Canada)

SEPTEMBER 2015

S	M	T	W	T	F	S
		1	2	3	4	5
6	7	8	9	10	11	12
13	14	15	16	17	18	19
20	21	22	23	24	25	26
27	28	29	30			

7 Labor Day
11 Patriot Day
13 National Grandparents' Day
14 Rosh Hashanah begins
23 Autumn begins
23 Yom Kippur begins
28 National Good Neighbor Day

OCTOBER 2015

S	M	T	W	T	F	S
				1	2	3
4	5	6	7	8	9	10
11	12	13	14	15	16	17
18	19	20	21	22	23	24
25	26	27	28	29	30	31

12 Columbus Day
12 Thanksgiving Day (Canada)
17 Sweetest Day
31 Halloween

NOVEMBER 2015

S	M	T	W	T	F	S
1	2	3	4	5	6	7
8	9	10	11	12	13	14
15	16	17	18	19	20	21
22	23	24	25	26	27	28
29	30					

1 Daylight Saving Time ends
3 Election Day
11 Veterans Day
11 Remembrance Day (Canada)
26 Thanksgiving Day

DECEMBER 2015

S	M	T	W	T	F	S
		1	2	3	4	5
6	7	8	9	10	11	12
13	14	15	16	17	18	19
20	21	22	23	24	25	26
27	28	29	30	31		

6 St. Nicholas' Day
6 Hanukkah begins
21 Winter begins
24 Christmas Eve
25 Christmas Day
26 Boxing Day (Canada)
31 New Year's Eve

Gift-Giving Guide

BIRTHSTONES AND FLOWERS

Month	Stone	Flower
January	Garnet (constancy)	Carnation (friendship)
February	Amethyst (sincerity)	Violet (modesty)
March	Bloodstone (courage)	Jonquil (affection)
April	Diamond (innocence)	Sweet pea (love)
May	Emerald (happiness)	Lily-of-the-valley (purity)
June	Pearl (purity)	Rose (devotion)
July	Ruby (nobility)	Larkspur (haughtiness)
August	Sardonyx (felicity)	Gladiolus (preparedness)
September	Sapphire (wisdom)	Aster (memories)
October	Opal (hope)	Calendula (constancy)
November	Topaz (fidelity)	Chrysanthemum (loveliness)
December	Turquoise (success)	Narcissus (precious moments)

ANNIVERSARY GIFTS

	Traditional	Modern		Traditional	Modern
1st	Paper	Clocks	13th	Lace	Textiles, furs
2nd	Cotton	China	14th	Ivory	Gold jewelry
3rd	Leather	Crystal, glass	15th	Crystal	Watches
4th	Books	Appliances	20th	China	Platinum
5th	Wood	Silverware	25th	Silver	Silver
6th	Candy, iron	Wood	30th	Pearl	Diamond
7th	Wool, copper	Desk sets	35th	Coral	Jade
8th	Bronze, pottery	Linens, lace	40th	Ruby	Ruby
9th	Pottery, willow	Leather	50th	Gold	Gold
10th	Tin, aluminum	Diamond jewelry	55th	Emerald	Emerald
11th	Steel	Fashion jewelry	60th	Diamond	Diamond
12th	Silk, linen	Pearls	75th	Diamond	Diamond

FAMILY CLOTHING SIZES

Family member	Shoes	Hosiery	Shirt, blouse or sweater	Suit, overcoat or dress	Gloves	Belt

Birthdays and Anniversaries

JANUARY

_____
_____
_____
_____
_____
_____
_____
_____
_____
_____

FEBRUARY

_____
_____
_____
_____
_____
_____
_____
_____
_____
_____

MARCH

_____
_____
_____
_____
_____
_____
_____
_____
_____
_____

JULY

_____
_____
_____
_____
_____
_____
_____
_____
_____
_____

AUGUST

_____
_____
_____
_____
_____
_____
_____
_____
_____
_____

SEPTEMBER

_____
_____
_____
_____
_____
_____
_____
_____
_____
_____

APRIL

_____
_____
_____
_____
_____
_____
_____
_____
_____
_____
_____
_____

MAY

_____
_____
_____
_____
_____
_____
_____
_____
_____
_____
_____
_____

JUNE

_____
_____
_____
_____
_____
_____
_____
_____
_____
_____
_____
_____

OCTOBER

_____
_____
_____
_____
_____
_____
_____
_____
_____
_____
_____
_____

NOVEMBER

_____
_____
_____
_____
_____
_____
_____
_____
_____
_____
_____
_____

DECEMBER

_____
_____
_____
_____
_____
_____
_____
_____
_____
_____
_____
_____

Important Phone Numbers

EMERGENCY NUMBERS

Ambulance _____

Fire Department _____

Hospital _____

Poison Control Center _____

Police Station _____

Rescue Squad _____

Other _____

DOCTORS

Chiropractor _____

Dentist _____

Optometrist/Ophthalmologist

_____

Oral Surgeon/Orthodontist

_____

Pharmacist _____

Physicians _____

_____

_____

_____

_____

Veterinarian _____

Other _____

HOME MAINTENANCE

Electrician _____

Exterminator _____

Hardware Store _____

Landlord/Building Superintendent

_____

Locksmith _____

Mechanic _____

Painter _____

Plumber _____

Recycling Center _____

Roofer _____

Snow Removal _____

Trash Removal _____

Other _____

APPLIANCE REPAIRS

Air Conditioning _____

Computer/Printer _____

Dishwasher _____

Heating _____

Microwave _____

Oven/Stove _____

Refrigerator/Freezer _____

Stereo System _____

TV/DVD/VCR _____

Washer/Dryer _____

Other _____

_____

_____

_____

_____

_____

GARRY WALTER

TAMMY WOLFE

SERVICES

Accountant _____

Banker/Broker _____

_____

_____

Dry Cleaner/Laundry _____

Financial Planner _____

Florist _____

Hair Stylist _____

Insurance Agent _____

Jeweler _____

Lawyer _____

Library _____

Nursery/Garden Center _____

Post Office _____

Real Estate Agent _____

Travel Agent _____

Other _____

_____

UTILITIES

Cable TV _____

Electric _____

Gas/Oil _____

Telephone _____

Water/Sewer _____

MORE IMPORTANT NUMBERS

Baby Sitters _____

_____

_____

_____

_____

Church _____

Neighbors _____

_____

_____

Relatives _____

_____

_____

_____

_____

_____

_____

Schools _____

_____

Weather _____

Other _____

_____

_____

_____

_____

Other Important Numbers

AUTOMOBILE IDENTIFICATION

Year/Make	License Plate Number	Vehicle Identification Number

CREDIT CARDS

Number	Issued by	Expires

IMPORTANT FAMILY NUMBERS

Name	Birth Date	Social Security	Driver's License

INSURANCE POLICIES

	Company	Agent's Name/ Number	Policy Number	Premium Amount	Premium Due
AUTO					
HOME					
LIFE					
MEDICAL					
DENTAL					
OTHER					

MONEY MANAGEMENT

	Financial Institution	Phone Number	Account Number
Checking			
Money Market			
Retirement			
Savings			
Other			

MORE IMPORTANT NUMBERS

January 2013

19 DEC
INR
2.6

Sunday	Monday	Tuesday	Wednesday	Thursday
	NOTE ①—	**1** RECYCLE	**2**	**3**
		New Year's Day		
6 "ESIGN" CONSENT—FOR WELLS FARGO SIGNES—7:30AM *Epiphany*	**7** CLEAN KITTY BOX WASH & FILL MOTIL 36 DAYS / 24 DAYS	**8**	**9**	**10**
13	**14** SIGNES FOR C&C —	**15** RECYCLE EARTHLINK	**16** INR 3.9 11:20AM 20 DAYS ON SINGLE FILTER DOT / LABEL 1:20	**17** TOOK DRUGS/LK TEST
20 ✓	**21** *Martin Luther King Jr. Day*	**22** INR 1:10 PM 2.3 WINDOW PIC'S KELLY KLISSN	**23** TALKED TO KELLY ON ANDERSON WINDOW ICING	**24** PRE'D "CD" EARTHLINK
27 CLEANED / ADDED (2) KITTY BOX	**28** DOT EYE 3:10 PM	**29** RECYCLE 8:30 AM PERRY ANDERSON WINDOW	**30** INR 1:1 PM 2.7	**31** DOT HAIR 11:45

16

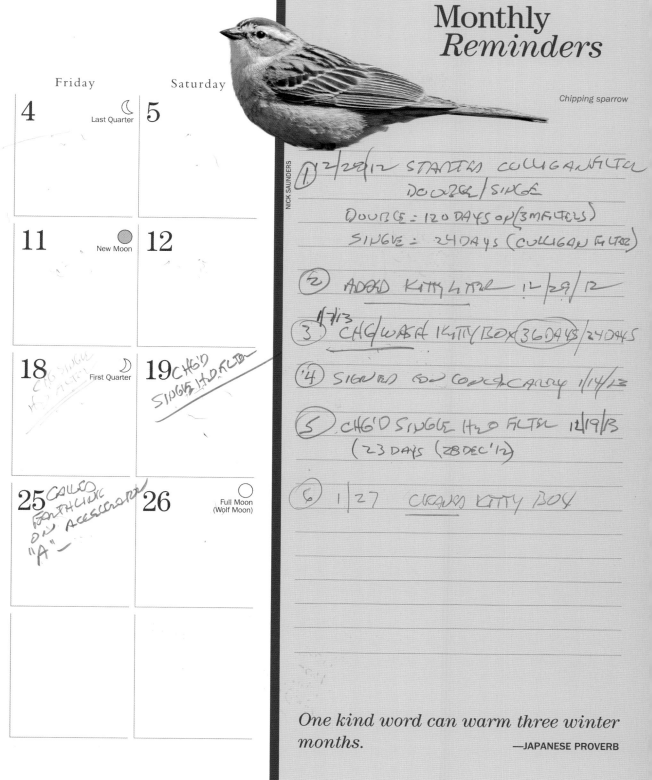

Monthly *Reminders*

Chipping sparrow

NICK SAUNDERS

Friday	Saturday
4 ☾ Last Quarter	**5**
11 ● New Moon	**12**
18 ☽ First Quarter *CHG SINGLE H₂O FILTER*	**19** *CHG'D SINGLE H₂O FILTER*
25 *CALLED EARTHLINK ON ACCESSORY "A"*	**26** ○ Full Moon (Wolf Moon)

Handwritten reminders:

1. 12/28/12 STARTED CULLIGAN FILTER DOUBLE/SINGLE
   DOUBLE = 120 DAYS OR (3 FILTERS)
   SINGLE = 24 DAYS (CULLIGAN FILTER)

2. ADDED KITTY LITTER 12/29/12

3. 1/7/13 CHG/WASH KITTY BOX (36 DAYS)/24 DAYS

4. SIGNED GUN CONCEAL CARRY 1/14/13

5. CHG'D SINGLE H₂O FILTER 12/19/13
   (23 DAYS (28 DEC '12)

6. 1/27 CLEANED KITTY BOX

One kind word can warm three winter months.

—JAPANESE PROVERB

February 2013

Sunday	Monday	Tuesday	Wednesday	Thursday
3 ☾ Last Quarter	**4** CLEAN TOILET FLOORS & COBWEBS / SENT E-MAIL TO READ	**5** CHG'D SINGER RCTL USED WASHED OUT	**6**	**7** 12
10 ● New Moon	**11** CHG'D WASHED OUT FILTER 2/5/13 W/ ANOTHER WASHED OUT FILTER	**12** DOT ZABEL RECYCLE *Abraham Lincoln's Birthday, 1809*	**13** DOT ZABEL *Ash Wednesday*	**14** CARALLIES OPERATION *Valentine's Day*
17 ☾ First Quarter	**18** ADDS TO LETTER BOX CHG'D CULLIGAN USED FILTER W/8ED COLD USED FILTER *Presidents Day*	**19**	**20** INR HARDERSON 09:30 TOM DOT HAIR 11:AM	**21** DOT @ ZABELS OFFICE
24 ✓	**25** ○ Full Moon (Snow Moon)	**26** 9:30 RECYCLE 1:30 TOMY ANDERSON	**27** INR 36 10:40	**28**

18

Monthly Reminders

Friday	Saturday
1	**2**
National Bird Feeding Month begins	*Groundhog Day*
8	**9** CQ TRAINING @ 0800 ~~WASHED KITTYBOX ADDED NEW LIT~~
15	**16**
22 *George Washington's Birthday, 1732*	**23** ④ IGNITION CONTROLS OUT FUES CONTACT

Primrose

Handwritten reminders:

USED FILTER — WASHED OUT FILTER

① 12/18 CHG. / ADDED TO LITTER BOX

② CHG'D USED CULLIGAN FILTER TO "USED" CUNO FILTER (STAYS)

③ CALLED ANDERSON ON 20 FEB SERVICE — SWITCHED TO 26 FEB 9:30 TO 1:30

④ 22 ON 23 FEB — IGNITION CONTROL OUT — FUES CONTACT

There's one good thing about snow. It makes your lawn look as nice as your neighbor's.

—CLYDE MOORE

BRAND X PICTURES

March 2013

Sunday	Monday	Tuesday	Wednesday	Thursday
3 CORRAL TRAINING	**4** ᛗᛟᚱᚲ ADDED LITTER ☽ Last Quarter	**5**	**6** INR 11:40 3.3	**7**
10 *Daylight Saving Time begins (Turn clocks ahead 1 hour)*	**11** ● New Moon	**12** RECYCLR ORG. SINGLE KLTR TOWNSHP MEET *Plant a Flower Day*	**13** TAX 15 AM WARD INR 1:40 3.2	**14** WASTED KITTY BOX ✓ 15 AM AVAIL OIL
17 *St. Patrick's Day*	**18**	**19** FAILED SWAP FT ☽ First Quarter	**20** INR 11:30 11:40 3.5 *Spring begins*	**21** DEP CACES DOUBO ISINGLE KTR ACTKS
24 *Palm Sunday* **31** *Easter*	**25** *Passover begins at sundown*	**26** STOP WASTE MGT. 1ST TRAIN-SWAP KIT 11 AM	**27** 12:50 INR 2.3 ○ Full Moon (Worm Moon)	**28** 2ND TRAIN NG @ SWAP FT 11 AM

Friday	Saturday
1	**2**
8 ~~SIGN UP~~ ~~SOUL FITNESS~~	**9**
15 ~~SIGN UP~~ ~~SWAP FIT~~	**16**
22 SIGN UP @ SWAP FIT	**23**
29 WILL DROP OFF TRASH CONTAINER	**30**
Good Friday	

11:40

11:00AM

Workout
w/Broncho
3/28

'ON 90 GAL AVAIL. 48 DAYS
SUPPLY @ 1½ GAL/DAY = 72 GAL
AVAIL.

3- 3/14 WASHED KITTY BOXES
PUT IN NEW LITTER

4-3/21 REPLACED DOUBLE FILTERS (33 DAYS)
REPLACED SINGLE FILTER (10 DAYS)

RDA-GID

...amellia

*The greatest gift of the garden is the
restoration of the five senses.* —HANNA RION

April 2013

Sunday	Monday	Tuesday	Wednesday	Thursday
	1 *April Fools' Day*	2 CHG'D SINGLE FILTER W/ WASHED OUT ON JTR	3 ☾ Last Quarter GIBSON BOTH CONTAINERS	4
7	8	9 TALKED TO JADEN 0900 WASH MGT TALKED TO MARIA ON AN CLINIC - WILL T CD	10 ● New Moon GIBSON BOTH CONTAINERS	11
14 GOD SHOWS W/ DANA	15 MOVE CONTAINER TO GARAGE *Income Tax Day*	16	17 GIBSON ADDED KITTY LITTER	18 First Qua DRI ZABEL
21 DEM FOR CLINCH	22 ✓ CHG- SINGLE FILTER 16 DAY *Earth Day*	23	24 GIBSON WM PICKED-UP CONTAINERS	25 Full M (Pink Mo IR 10:50 1.7
28	29	30		

22

Monthly Reminders

Friday	Saturday
5	6 CHG SINGLE FILTER
12	13 GUN SHO w/DAVE ✓
	Thomas Jefferson's Birthday, 1743
19	20
26	27
National Arbor Day *Naturalist John James Audubon's Birthday, 1785*	

Nemesia

2 APRL - CHG SINGLE FILTER
w/WASHED OUT FILTER

6 APRIL   CHG SINGLE FILTER (50 DAYS)
22 APRIL   CHG SINGLE FILTER (16 DAYS)

Rainbows apologize for angry skies.

—SYLVIA VOIROL

May 2013

Sunday	Monday	Tuesday	Wednesday	Thursday
			1 GIBSON $1:10 INR 2.0 w/Trash RECYCLE *May Day*	2 Last Quar
5 *Cinco de Mayo* *Be Kind to Animals Week begins*	6	7	8	9 ✓SINGLE FILTER CHG'd SINGLE FILTER New Mo *Ascension Day*
12 *Mother's Day*	13	14	15 GIBSON RECYCLE	16
19 *Pentecost*	20 *Victoria Day (Canada)*	21	22	23
26 CHG'd SINGLE FILTER 180 DAYS	27 *Memorial Day*	28 INR 1:10 1.65	29 RECYCLE INR	30

24

Friday	Saturday
3 ✓	4
10 ✓	11

International Migratory Bird Day |
| 17 ✓ | 18 ☾ First Quarter ✓

Armed Forces Day |
| 24 | 25 ○ Full Moon (Flower Moon) |
| 31 ☾ Last Quarter | |

ROLAND JORDAHL

Monthly *Reminders*

Rose-breasted grosbeak

1- 9 MAY — CHG'D SINGLE FILTER
(21 MAY CHG'D DOUBLE FILTER — 50 DAYS)

2- CHG SINGLE FILTER 20TH 18 DAYS

3- SERVICED WATER SOFTNER VENTURI

A bird does not sing because it has an answer. It sings because it has a song.

—CHINESE PROVERB

June 2013

Sunday	Monday	Tuesday	Wednesday	Thursday
2 *National Garden Week begins*	**3**	**4** DR. PALLAS 11:20 11:10 INR 2.01	**5**	**6**
9 *Children's Sunday*	**10**	**11**	**12** RECYCLE	**13**
16 First Quarter *Father's Day*	**17**	**18**	**19**	**20**
23 Full Moon (Strawberry Moon) **30** Last Quarter	**24** *St. Jean Baptiste Day (Canada)*	**25**	**26** RECYCLE CAGE SINGER FILTER	**27**

Monthly Reminders

Friday	Saturday
	1
7	**8** DACE/KAM 6:30PM ○ New Moon
14 CHG'D SIPGLE FILTER *Flag Day*	**15**
21 *Summer begins (Longest day of the year)*	**22**
28	**29**

JAMES MARTIN

1 — 14 JUN CHG'D SINGLE FILTER
   (20 DAYS — 26 MAY)
   (DOUBLE FILTER @ 87 DAYS)

2 — 26 JUN — CHG'D SINGLE FILTER (13 DAYS)

Just like the butterfly, I too will awaken in my own time. —DEBORAH CHASKIN

July 2013

Sunday	Monday	Tuesday	Wednesday	Thursday
	1 *Canada Day*	**2**	**3**	**4** *Independence Day*
7	**8** ● New Moon	**9** *INV 11:50 3.6*	**10** *DOTS HAIR 3:30PM RECYCLE CAG'D H2O FILTERS*	**11**
14	**15** ☾ First Quarter	**16**	**17**	**18**
21	**22** ○ Full Moon (Buck Moon) *10:40 INV 2.1*	**23**	**24** *RECYCLE*	**25**
28	**29** ☾ Last Quarter *CAG'D SINGLE MOTH*	**30**	**31**	

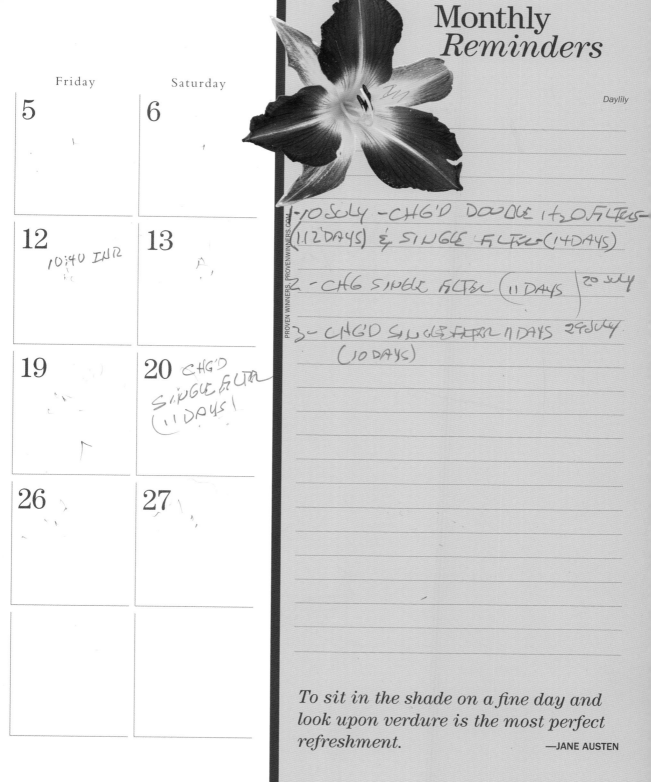

Friday	Saturday
5	6
12 10:40 INR	13
19	20 CHG'D SINGLE FLTR (11 DAYS)
26	27

Monthly Reminders

Daylily

1-10 JULY - CHG'D DOODLE 1 & 20 FILTERS (12 DAYS) & SINGLE FILTER (14 DAYS)

2- CHG SINGLE FILTER (11 DAYS) 20 JULY

3- CHG'D SINGLE FILTER 11 DAYS 29 JULY (10 DAYS)

To sit in the shade on a fine day and look upon verdure is the most perfect refreshment.

—JANE AUSTEN

August 2013

Sunday	Monday	Tuesday	Wednesday	Thursday
				1
4	5 INR 2.3 11:10 — *Civic Holiday (Canada)*	6 New Moon	7 RECYCLE	8
11	12 ROH FURNACE	13	14 First Quarter	15 ROTS HAM 3 PM
18	19 DOT 3:10 EYES	20 Full Moon (Sturgeon Moon)	21 RECYCLE	22
25 DOT KIM HEATHER?	26	27	28 Last Quarter	29

Friday	Saturday
2 BOUGHT BRUTE LAWN MOWER / BOUGHT MTD DETHACHER	**3** ERLING ESTIMATING FURNACE-OIC/LP WILL GET BACK W/ME
9	**10**
16	**17**
23 DOT HAIR 11:15 CALLED RON	**24**
30 DOT HAIR H.S	**31** DOT TRIM HEATHER ?

Common buckeye

PAT GARNER

Nature does not hurry, yet everything is accomplished.

—LAO TZU

September 2013

Sunday	Monday	Tuesday	Wednesday	Thursday
1	2	3	4 *Recycle*	5 New Mo~ *INR 11:20 2.4*
	Labor Day		*Rosh Hashanah begins at sundown*	
8	9	10 *DOT-DENTAL 2:PM*	11	12 First Qua~
National Grandparents' Day			*Patriot Day*	
15	16	17	18 *Recycle*	19 Full Mo~ (Harvest Mo~ *DOT HAIR 3:PM*
22 *Wed'd Simple Filter*	23	24	25 *DOT'S FIRE*	26 Last Qua~
Autumn begins				
29	30			

Friday	Saturday
6 DOT HAIR 11:15	**7** CHG SINGLE FILTER
13 DOT HAIR 11:15 COREEN/DAUGHTER WEDN *Yom Kippur begins at sundown*	**14**
20 C HAIR 10 AM	**21**
27 DOT HAIR 11:15	**28** *National Good Neighbor Day*

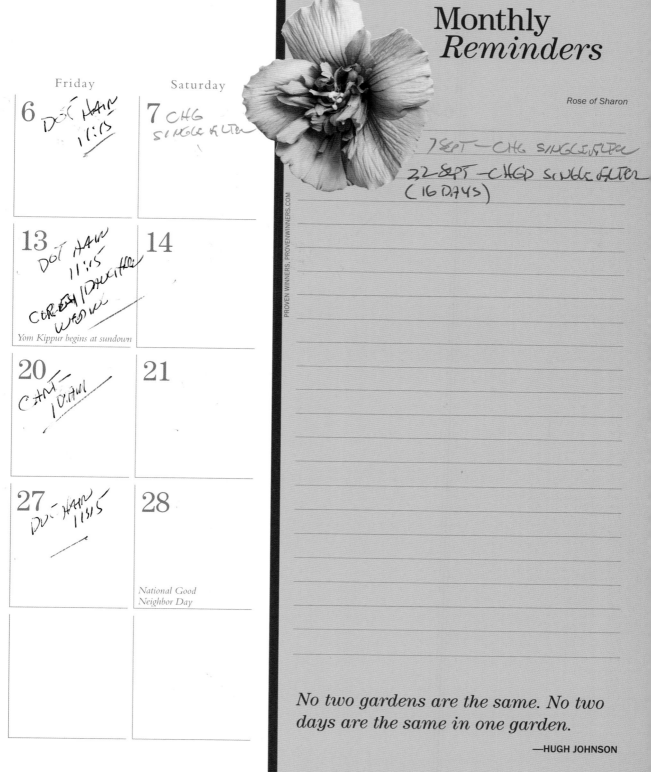

Monthly
Reminders

Rose of Sharon

7 SEPT — CHG SINGLE FILTER
22 SEPT — CHGD SINGLE FILTER
(16 DAYS)

No two gardens are the same. No two days are the same in one garden.

—HUGH JOHNSON

October 2013

Sunday	Monday	Tuesday	Wednesday	Thursday
		1	2 RECYCLE 2:3 INR 11:4am ELECT LINES MARKED	3 PHONE LINES MARKED
6	7	8 L.P. TANK INST'L ✓	9 INST'L LP 380GA	10
13	14 *Columbus Day* *Thanksgiving Day (Canada)*	15 (87) INSTALLED LP FURNACE GAS	16 DR ZABEL 1:20 PM RECYCLE	17 TIRES
20	21	22 ✓ LP READ (75)	23 DOT BRS 1:10	24
27	28	29 ✓ L.P. CALL WANDA TAXES MON 7,14 11AM LINE BACKER 5637 2167 REMODEL 10:15an	30 DOT BRS ADD INR 10:40 RECYCLE 2.0	31 *Halloween*

CHG'D DOUBLE FILTER & WASHED OUT SINGLE FILTER

↓

90 DAYS

Friday

4 *New Moon*

DOT ↑
ASPEN 11:15
CALL "FANK"
FOR MON/TUES

11 *First Quarter*

DOT APPT
11:05
~~CHECK~~
INSTL NEW
SINGLE FILTER

18 *Full Moon (Hunter's Moon)*

Saturday

5
RANCHERO
7:00 P.M.

12

19
CHG'D
SINGLE FILTER

Sweetest Day

25
DOT COLON
9 AM

26 *Last Quarter*

Monthly Reminders

Japanese maple leaf

RDA-GID

4 OCT — CHG'D DOUBLE FILTER (90 DAYS)
& WASHED OUT SINGLE FILTER

11 OCT — INSTALLED NEW SINGLE
FILTER (WASHED OUT FILTER
LASTED 8 DAYS)

19 OCT CHG'D SINGLE FILTER (8 DAYS)

(23)

Autumn is a second spring when every leaf is a flower.
—ALBERT CAMUS

November 2013

Sunday	Monday	Tuesday	Wednesday	Thursday
			30TH RECYCLE	
3 New Moon *Daylight Saving Time ends (Turn clocks back 1 hour)*	**4**	**5** SERVICED MTD BRUTE SWIVEL WHEEL (NEW) MANTIS & FIELD CUTTER *Election Day*	**6**	**7** ✓ VLP
10 First Quarter	**11** CHG'D SINGLE FILTER *Veterans Day* *Remembrance Day (Canada)*	**12**	**13** RECYCLE	**14**
17 Full Moon (Beaver Moon)	**18**	**19** CHG'D SINGLE FILTER ✓ LP @ 68 - (9 DAYS)	**20**	**21**
24	**25** DR. SCHAFFLER 1:30 Last Quarter	**26**	**27** RECYCLE EUR DR MET (RUSS) *Hanukkah begins at sundown*	**28** *Thanksgiving Day*

Friday	Saturday
1 CHG'D SINGLE FILTER (13 DAYS) *All Saints Day*	**2**
8 ✓L.P. @12/71 (75)	**9**
15	**16**
22	**23**
29 FILLED L.P. 112.2 GAL	**30** CHG'D SINGLE FILTER (12 DAYS) 112 GAL/48 DAYS 2.05 GAL/DAY

Monthly Reminders

Common redpoll

MARTINE COCHRANE

1 NOV — CHG SINGLE FILTER (13 DAYS)

11 NOV — CHG. SINGLE FILTER (11 DAYS)

15 NOV — CHG'D SINGLE FILTER (9 DAYS)

30 NOV — CHG'D SINGLE FILTER (12 DAYS)

23
29
/5

If I had to choose, I would rather have birds than airplanes. —CHARLES LINDBERGH

December 2013

Sunday	Monday	Tuesday	Wednesday	Thursday
			30 Oct	
1 *Advent begins*	**2** New Moon	**3**	**4**	**5**
8 CHG SINGLE FILM 9 DAYS	**9** X:PM INP CANCELLED 8:PM	**10** CALLED OD AP BILL #22 DISCOUNT AGPORTERS	**11** RECYCLE	**12** L.P. 75
15	**16**	**17** TALKED TO VISA ON REWARDS POINT - CALL AGAIN - FEB/MAR 2014 · Full Moon (Cold Moon)	**18** DR SCHADFE DOTS CHG	**19** 2:15 2:00 DR PILGRIM CHG SINGLE FILM 120
22	**23** DR SCOT DOT MRI 3:PM	**24** CHG D SINGLE+DOUBLE FILMS SEE NOTES 3 4 *Christmas Eve*	**25** RECYCLE · Last Quarter *Christmas Day*	**26** *Boxing Day (Canada)*
29	**30**	**31** *New Year's Eve*		

38

Friday	Saturday
6	7
St. Nicholas' Day	
13	14
20	21
	Winter begins (Shortest day of the year)
27	28

Monthly Reminders

INR 30TH OCt

① 12 DEC LP @ 75

② CHG SINGLE FILTER (12 DAY)
(12/9)

③ CHGD SINGE FILTER (60 DAYS)

④ CHG DOUBLE FILTER (82 DAYS)

$3\frac{1}{2}$

$3\frac{3}{5}$

32 DAYS NOV 29
DEC 31+1

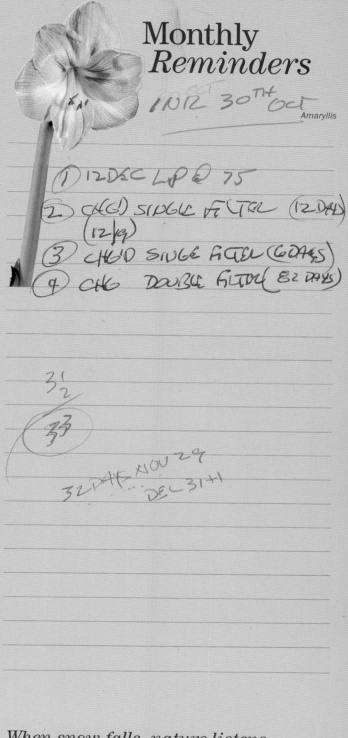

When snow falls, nature listens.

—ANTOINETTE VAN KLEEFF

January

Friends

On this the coldest day of the year,
My feathered friends seem to have disappeared.
But when it warms, perched in the trees,
There they will be, swaying in the breeze.

They flit and they dash all over the place,
And watching them always puts a smile on my face.
Wishing at times I was as free as they,
To try my wings, to do nothing but play.

A kaleidoscope of color they often make.
Yellow, blue and red—my soul they take.
With their sweet songs and humbling ways,
The joy they bring fulfills my days.

—SANDY STOY
Wilmington, North Carolina

Mourning doves by Kit Breen

Backyard
journal

December 2012

31
Monday

New Year's Eve

1
Tuesday

New Year's Day

2
Wednesday

3
Thursday

January 2013

4
Friday

5
Saturday

6
Sunday

Epiphany

BAILEY NURSERIES

An appealing, upright shrub, redtwig dogwood's vivid red branches and whitish-blue fruit (which form on the mature growth) create an eye-catching cool-season show. This fast and fuss-free grower prefers relatively moist soil and a sunny site.

DECEMBER 2012						
S	M	T	W	T	F	S
						1
2	3	4	5	6	7	8
9	10	11	12	13	14	15
16	17	18	19	20	21	22
23	24	25	26	27	28	29
30	31					

JANUARY 2013						
S	M	T	W	T	F	S
		1	2	3	4	5
6	7	8	9	10	11	12
13	14	15	16	17	18	19
20	21	22	23	24	25	26
27	28	29	30	31		

FEBRUARY 2013						
S	M	T	W	T	F	S
					1	2
3	4	5	6	7	8	9
10	11	12	13	14	15	16
17	18	19	20	21	22	23
24	25	26	27	28		

Backyard journal

_____
_____
_____
_____
_____
_____
_____
_____
_____
_____
_____
_____
_____
_____
_____
_____
_____
_____
_____
_____
_____
_____
_____
_____

January 2013

7
Monday

8
Tuesday

9
Wednesday

10
Thursday

11
Friday

12
Saturday

13
Sunday

Sunflower and nyjer seeds encourage red crossbills to visit backyard feeders in the wintertime, when they inhabit much of the U.S. and Canada. The birds' twisted bills allow them to easily crack open cones and other seeds in their natural diet.

DECEMBER 2012

S	M	T	W	T	F	S
						1
2	3	4	5	6	7	8
9	10	11	12	13	14	15
16	17	18	19	20	21	22
23	24	25	26	27	28	29
30	31					

JANUARY 2013

S	M	T	W	T	F	S
		1	2	3	4	5
6	7	8	9	10	11	12
13	14	15	16	17	18	19
20	21	22	23	24	25	26
27	28	29	30	31		

FEBRUARY 2013

S	M	T	W	T	F	S
					1	2
3	4	5	6	7	8	9
10	11	12	13	14	15	16
17	18	19	20	21	22	23
24	25	26	27	28		

Backyard journal

_____
_____
_____
_____
_____
_____
_____
_____
_____
_____
_____
_____
_____
_____
_____
_____
_____
_____
_____
_____
_____
_____
_____
_____
_____
_____
_____
_____
_____
_____
_____

January 2013

14
Monday

15
Tuesday

16
Wednesday

17
Thursday

18
Friday

19
Saturday

20
Sunday

Early blooms earn hellebore the common names of Lenten and Christmas rose. Flowers come in an array of shapes and colors, from pink to black to green. No matter which type you choose, you'll appreciate this dazzler's evergreen foliage.

DECEMBER 2012						
S	M	T	W	T	F	S
						1
2	3	4	5	6	7	8
9	10	11	12	13	14	15
16	17	18	19	20	21	22
23	24	25	26	27	28	29
30	31					

JANUARY 2013						
S	M	T	W	T	F	S
		1	2	3	4	5
6	7	8	9	10	11	12
13	14	15	16	17	18	19
20	21	22	23	24	25	26
27	28	29	30	31		

FEBRUARY 2013						
S	M	T	W	T	F	S
					1	2
3	4	5	6	7	8	9
10	11	12	13	14	15	16
17	18	19	20	21	22	23
24	25	26	27	28		

January 2013

21
Monday

Martin Luther King Jr. Day

22
Tuesday

23
Wednesday

24
Thursday

25
Friday

26
Saturday

27
Sunday

The northern flicker's markings vary across the continent. Eastern and western males sport bold black and red "mustaches," respectively. Also, in the East, the wings and tail include yellow feathers (seen here); these are red in the West.

DECEMBER 2012						
S	M	T	W	T	F	S
						1
2	3	4	5	6	7	8
9	10	11	12	13	14	15
16	17	18	19	20	21	22
23	24	25	26	27	28	29
30	31					

JANUARY 2013						
S	M	T	W	T	F	S
		1	2	3	4	5
6	7	8	9	10	11	12
13	14	15	16	17	18	19
20	21	22	23	24	25	26
27	28	29	30	31		

FEBRUARY 2013						
S	M	T	W	T	F	S
					1	2
3	4	5	6	7	8	9
10	11	12	13	14	15	16
17	18	19	20	21	22	23
24	25	26	27	28		

February

Reaching for Spring

Even in winter I have visions of spring,
Flowers in bloom and birds on the wing.

I find myself looking for signs of new growth,
Under the leaves, the mulch or both.

I remember the colors and scents of last year,
When bulbs already planted begin to appear.

Not even thinking of the hard work and sweat,
It's the beauty of flowers that I can't forget.

I walk each morning down my garden path,
Watching the birds as they take a bath.

Touching a bloom that has opened its face,
To be admired, but not in haste.

I love my garden, the flowers, the birds,
More than I could ever put into words.

—MARABETH INGRE PLEMMONS
Hendersonville, North Carolina

Snowdrops by GAP Photos Ltd.

Backyard journal

_____
_____
_____
_____
_____
_____
_____
_____
_____
_____
_____
_____
_____
_____
_____
_____
_____
_____
_____
_____
_____
_____
_____
_____

January 2013

28
Monday

29
Tuesday

30
Wednesday

31
Thursday

February 2013

1
Friday

2
Saturday

Groundhog Day

3
Sunday

Love roses but not the hassle that comes with them? Consider the rugosa rose, a shrubby species that flourishes just about anywhere. In winter, your landscape will be dotted with bright-red rose hips like the ones here, courtesy of this resilient grower.

JANUARY 2013						
S	M	T	W	T	F	S
		1	2	3	4	5
6	7	8	9	10	11	12
13	14	15	16	17	18	19
20	21	22	23	24	25	26
27	28	29	30	31		

FEBRUARY 2013						
S	M	T	W	T	F	S
					1	2
3	4	5	6	7	8	9
10	11	12	13	14	15	16
17	18	19	20	21	22	23
24	25	26	27	28		

MARCH 2013						
S	M	T	W	T	F	S
					1	2
3	4	5	6	7	8	9
10	11	12	13	14	15	16
17	18	19	20	21	22	23
24	25	26	27	28	29	30
31						

Backyard journal

_____
_____
_____
_____
_____
_____
_____
_____
_____
_____
_____
_____
_____
_____
_____
_____
_____
_____
_____
_____
_____
_____
_____
_____
_____
_____

February 2013

4
Monday

5
Tuesday

6
Wednesday

7
Thursday

8
Friday

9
Saturday

10
Sunday

LAURENZ BAARS

Similar plumage
of male and female pine siskins makes the sexes hard to tell apart—so look for more yellow on males. In winter, these tiny fliers, who belong to the finch family, span almost the entire continent. They fly north to breed in summer.

JANUARY 2013

S	M	T	W	T	F	S
		1	2	3	4	5
6	7	8	9	10	11	12
13	14	15	16	17	18	19
20	21	22	23	24	25	26
27	28	29	30	31		

FEBRUARY 2013

S	M	T	W	T	F	S
					1	2
3	4	5	6	7	8	9
10	11	12	13	14	15	16
17	18	19	20	21	22	23
24	25	26	27	28		

MARCH 2013

S	M	T	W	T	F	S
					1	2
3	4	5	6	7	8	9
10	11	12	13	14	15	16
17	18	19	20	21	22	23
24	25	26	27	28	29	30
31						

Backyard journal

_____
_____
_____
_____
_____
_____
_____
_____
_____
_____
_____
_____
_____
_____
_____
_____
_____
_____
_____
_____
_____
_____
_____
_____
_____

February 2013

11
Monday

12
Tuesday

Abraham Lincoln's Birthday, 1809

13
Wednesday

Ash Wednesday

14
Thursday

Valentine's Day

15
Friday

16
Saturday

17
Sunday

Just when you're convinced spring will never arrive, witch hazel explodes with masses of fragrant flowers in shades of yellow, red and copper. Some cultivars bloom as early as January and hold onto their ribbon-petal blossoms until March.

JANUARY 2013

S	M	T	W	T	F	S
		1	2	3	4	5
6	7	8	9	10	11	12
13	14	15	16	17	18	19
20	21	22	23	24	25	26
27	28	29	30	31		

FEBRUARY 2013

S	M	T	W	T	F	S
					1	2
3	4	5	6	7	8	9
10	11	12	13	14	15	16
17	18	19	20	21	22	23
24	25	26	27	28		

MARCH 2013

S	M	T	W	T	F	S
					1	2
3	4	5	6	7	8	9
10	11	12	13	14	15	16
17	18	19	20	21	22	23
24	25	26	27	28	29	30
31						

February 2013

18
Monday

Presidents Day

19
Tuesday

20
Wednesday

21
Thursday

22
Friday

George Washington's Birthday, 1732

23
Saturday

24
Sunday

RDA-GID

Delicate late-winter or early-spring bloomers, cyclamen prefer part shade. A drift of these tuberous woodland perennials will happily peek out from under trees and shrubs. Pink, purple or white flowers nod above leaves that resemble lily pads.

JANUARY 2013						
S	M	T	W	T	F	S
		1	2	3	4	5
6	7	8	9	10	11	12
13	14	15	16	17	18	19
20	21	22	23	24	25	26
27	28	29	30	31		

FEBRUARY 2013						
S	M	T	W	T	F	S
					1	2
3	4	5	6	7	8	9
10	11	12	13	14	15	16
17	18	19	20	21	22	23
24	25	26	27	28		

MARCH 2013						
S	M	T	W	T	F	S
					1	2
3	4	5	6	7	8	9
10	11	12	13	14	15	16
17	18	19	20	21	22	23
24	25	26	27	28	29	30
31						

March

Emergence of Spring

Soaring through the air on gossamer wings,
Butterflies float, as songbirds sing.
What a glorious sound to start a new day,
As they fluff their feathers in a coquettish way.
The glistening dewdrops kissing each flower,
Could keep me enchanted hour upon hour.
With colors so vibrant, a palette so pure,
Nature so radiant, has a magnetic lure.
My heart is in rapture, with so many hues.
Springtime is for sitting and enjoying the view.

—**E. SUE COLTON**
Eufaula, Oklahoma

Pearl crescent by David Stuckel

February 2013

25
Monday

26
Tuesday

27
Wednesday

28
Thursday

March 2013

1
Friday

2
Saturday

3
Sunday

NICK SAUNDERS

Every spring, clay-colored sparrows can be found throughout the Great Plains, winging their way north from Mexico. The destination: prairie brushlands of the upper U.S. and Canada, where they will breed, returning to warmer climates in autumn.

FEBRUARY 2013						
S	M	T	W	T	F	S
					1	2
3	4	5	6	7	8	9
10	11	12	13	14	15	16
17	18	19	20	21	22	23
24	25	26	27	28		

MARCH 2013						
S	M	T	W	T	F	S
					1	2
3	4	5	6	7	8	9
10	11	12	13	14	15	16
17	18	19	20	21	22	23
24	25	26	27	28	29	30
31						

APRIL 2013						
S	M	T	W	T	F	S
	1	2	3	4	5	6
7	8	9	10	11	12	13
14	15	16	17	18	19	20
21	22	23	24	25	26	27
28	29	30				

Backyard
journal

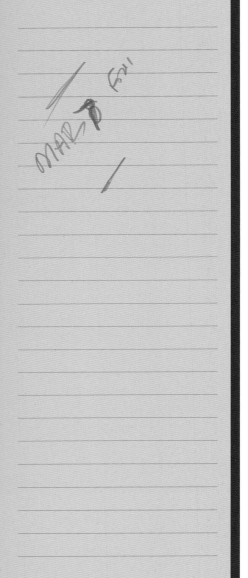

4
Monday

5
Tuesday

6
Wednesday

7
Thursday

8
Friday

9
Saturday

10
Sunday

Daylight Saving Time begins (Turn clocks ahead 1 hour.)

RDA-GID

Hardy, playful crocuses announce warmer weather's arrival with their glossy, cup-shaped blooms. Create a big impact with a naturalized sweep across the lawn, densely packed border or sunny planter display near your front doorstep.

FEBRUARY 2013

S	M	T	W	T	F	S
					1	2
3	4	5	6	7	8	9
10	11	12	13	14	15	16
17	18	19	20	21	22	23
24	25	26	27	28		

MARCH 2013

S	M	T	W	T	F	S
					1	2
3	4	5	6	7	8	9
10	11	12	13	14	15	16
17	18	19	20	21	22	23
24	25	26	27	28	29	30
31						

APRIL 2013

S	M	T	W	T	F	S
	1	2	3	4	5	6
7	8	9	10	11	12	13
14	15	16	17	18	19	20
21	22	23	24	25	26	27
28	29	30				

Backyard journal

11
Monday

12
Tuesday

Plant a Flower Day

13
Wednesday

14
Thursday

15
Friday

16
Saturday

17
Sunday

St. Patrick's Day

LAURENZ BAARS

Backyard birders
in nearly all regions of the U.S. and Canada have the chance to spot a yellow-rumped warbler each year. In the South, where they spend the winter, these warblers eat seedcakes. During their northern summers, they frequent birdbaths.

FEBRUARY 2013						
S	M	T	W	T	F	S
					1	2
3	4	5	6	7	8	9
10	11	12	13	14	15	16
17	18	19	20	21	22	23
24	25	26	27	28		

MARCH 2013						
S	M	T	W	T	F	S
					1	2
3	4	5	6	7	8	9
10	11	12	13	14	15	16
17	18	19	20	21	22	23
24	25	26	27	28	29	30
31						

APRIL 2013						
S	M	T	W	T	F	S
	1	2	3	4	5	6
7	8	9	10	11	12	13
14	15	16	17	18	19	20
21	22	23	24	25	26	27
28	29	30				

Backyard journal

March 2013

18
Monday

19
Tuesday

20
Wednesday

Spring begins

21
Thursday

22
Friday

23
Saturday

24
Sunday

Palm Sunday

When forsythia
branches bloom, you can be certain that Old Man Winter is getting ready to go. This is one of the first shrubs to flower in spring, at a time when its golden bell-shaped blossoms are an especially welcome sight.

FEBRUARY 2013						
S	M	T	W	T	F	S
					1	2
3	4	5	6	7	8	9
10	11	12	13	14	15	16
17	18	19	20	21	22	23
24	25	26	27	28		

MARCH 2013						
S	M	T	W	T	F	S
					1	2
3	4	5	6	7	8	9
10	11	12	13	14	15	16
17	18	19	20	21	22	23
24	25	26	27	28	29	30
31						

APRIL 2013						
S	M	T	W	T	F	S
	1	2	3	4	5	6
7	8	9	10	11	12	13
14	15	16	17	18	19	20
21	22	23	24	25	26	27
28	29	30				

March 2013

25
Monday

26
Tuesday

Passover begins at sundown

27
Wednesday

28
Thursday

29
Friday

Good Friday

30
Saturday

31
Sunday

Easter

RDA-GID

A spring garden

must-have, cheerful pansies' colors run the gamut from multihued to monochromatic. Most perform best in cooler weather, so consider replanting them in the fall, when blooms can persist into winter— even in the North.

FEBRUARY 2013						
S	M	T	W	T	F	S
					1	2
3	4	5	6	7	8	9
10	11	12	13	14	15	16
17	18	19	20	21	22	23
24	25	26	27	28		

MARCH 2013						
S	M	T	W	T	F	S
					1	2
3	4	5	6	7	8	9
10	11	12	13	14	15	16
17	18	19	20	21	22	23
24	25	26	27	28	29	30
31						

APRIL 2013						
S	M	T	W	T	F	S
	1	2	3	4	5	6
7	8	9	10	11	12	13
14	15	16	17	18	19	20
21	22	23	24	25	26	27
28	29	30				

April

A Rainbow on Wings

Perching on my feeder,
Flitting tree to tree,
Nature's sparkling gems,
A glorious sight to see.

Their songs are so lilting,
Bringing joy and good cheer,
Welcoming each spring season,
Year after year.

—LIL CURRIER
Madison, Wisconsin

Male American goldfinch by Linda Freshwater Arndt

Backyard journal

_____
_____
_____
_____
_____
_____
_____
_____
_____
_____
_____
_____
_____
_____
_____
_____
_____
_____
_____
_____
_____
_____
_____
_____
_____
_____
_____
_____

April 2013

1
Monday

April Fools' Day

2
Tuesday

3
Wednesday

4
Thursday

5
Friday

6
Saturday

7
Sunday

BAILEY NURSERIES

A true wildlife
favorite, the redbud seems to burst with a profusion of purple, red or white blossoms before its leaves emerge, attracting many nectar seekers. In the months that follow, songbirds visit to eat the ripened seeds.

MARCH 2013

S	M	T	W	T	F	S
					1	2
3	4	5	6	7	8	9
10	11	12	13	14	15	16
17	18	19	20	21	22	23
24	25	26	27	28	29	30
31						

APRIL 2013

S	M	T	W	T	F	S
	1	2	3	4	5	6
7	8	9	10	11	12	13
14	15	16	17	18	19	20
21	22	23	24	25	26	27
28	29	30				

MAY 2013

S	M	T	W	T	F	S
			1	2	3	4
5	6	7	8	9	10	11
12	13	14	15	16	17	18
19	20	21	22	23	24	25
26	27	28	29	30	31	

Backyard journal

April 2013

8
Monday

9
Tuesday

10
Wednesday

11
Thursday

12
Friday

13
Saturday

Thomas Jefferson's Birthday, 1743

14
Sunday

Watch for these black, red-orange and white butterflies fluttering nearby— especially around hops and nettles, their host plants. Red admirals migrate, so spring is the season when they make the trip north from Central America.

MARCH 2013						
S	M	T	W	T	F	S
					1	2
3	4	5	6	7	8	9
10	11	12	13	14	15	16
17	18	19	20	21	22	23
24	25	26	27	28	29	30
31						

APRIL 2013						
S	M	T	W	T	F	S
	1	2	3	4	5	6
7	8	9	10	11	12	13
14	15	16	17	18	19	20
21	22	23	24	25	26	27
28	29	30				

MAY 2013						
S	M	T	W	T	F	S
			1	2	3	4
5	6	7	8	9	10	11
12	13	14	15	16	17	18
19	20	21	22	23	24	25
26	27	28	29	30	31	

April 2013

15
Monday

Income Tax Day

16
Tuesday

17
Wednesday

18
Thursday

19
Friday

20
Saturday

21
Sunday

It's no wonder that daffodils are among gardeners' most beloved spring flowers, whether they're yellow, white, orange or pink. Not only are daffodils easy to grow in most soil types, but the bulbs are toxic— backyard critters will leave them alone.

MARCH 2013						
S	M	T	W	T	F	S
					1	2
3	4	5	6	7	8	9
10	11	12	13	14	15	16
17	18	19	20	21	22	23
24	25	26	27	28	29	30
31						

APRIL 2013						
S	M	T	W	T	F	S
	1	2	3	4	5	6
7	8	9	10	11	12	13
14	15	16	17	18	19	20
21	22	23	24	25	26	27
28	29	30				

MAY 2013						
S	M	T	W	T	F	S
			1	2	3	4
5	6	7	8	9	10	11
12	13	14	15	16	17	18
19	20	21	22	23	24	25
26	27	28	29	30	31	

April 2013

22
Monday

Earth Day

23
Tuesday

24
Wednesday

25
Thursday

26
Friday

Arbor Day
Naturalist John James Audubon's Birthday, 1785

27
Saturday

28
Sunday

TED ROSE

Bluebirds are
early nesters, so parents can raise at least two broods each year. Males deliver food to incubating females and participate equally in feeding nestlings. Newly hatched eastern bluebirds leave the nest in 15 to 20 days.

MARCH 2013

S	M	T	W	T	F	S
					1	2
3	4	5	6	7	8	9
10	11	12	13	14	15	16
17	18	19	20	21	22	23
24	25	26	27	28	29	30
31						

APRIL 2013

S	M	T	W	T	F	S
	1	2	3	4	5	6
7	8	9	10	11	12	13
14	15	16	17	18	19	20
21	22	23	24	25	26	27
28	29	30				

MAY 2013

S	M	T	W	T	F	S
			1	2	3	4
5	6	7	8	9	10	11
12	13	14	15	16	17	18
19	20	21	22	23	24	25
26	27	28	29	30	31	

May

Bloom

Sight
and sound
and touch and taste
awaken bloom
as spring
is plucked up
by fluffed white clouds
refracting light to spin
into a multitude of brightly
colored threads…patterns
tightly interlaced by
the warp and woof
of nature's busy loom.

—ANNE SELDEN
Mechanicsburg, Pennsylvania

Tulip by GAP Photos Ltd.

Backyard journal

April 2013

29
Monday

30
Tuesday

1
Wednesday

May Day

2
Thursday

May 2013

3
Friday

4
Saturday

5
Sunday

Cinco de Mayo
Be Kind to Animals Week begins

Sweet-smelling blossoms on this old-fashioned ground cover might look delicate, but don't be deceived: Lily-of-the-valley is tough as nails. For clusters growing beneath trees and shrubs, provide a dose of fertilizer each spring for the best show.

APRIL 2013

S	M	T	W	T	F	S
	1	2	3	4	5	6
7	8	9	10	11	12	13
14	15	16	17	18	19	20
21	22	23	24	25	26	27
28	29	30				

MAY 2013

S	M	T	W	T	F	S
			1	2	3	4
5	6	7	8	9	10	11
12	13	14	15	16	17	18
19	20	21	22	23	24	25
26	27	28	29	30	31	

JUNE 2013

S	M	T	W	T	F	S
						1
2	3	4	5	6	7	8
9	10	11	12	13	14	15
16	17	18	19	20	21	22
23	24	25	26	27	28	29
30						

Backyard journal

May 2013

6
Monday

7
Tuesday

8
Wednesday

9
Thursday

Ascension Day

10
Friday

11
Saturday

International Migratory Bird Day

12
Sunday

Mother's Day

Hard to miss,
yellow warblers gravitate to water. Invite a nesting pair to your yard simply by displaying a birdbath. Or better yet, provide access to moving water such as a stream or a bubbling fountain. These fliers prefer to nest in willow thickets.

APRIL 2013						
S	M	T	W	T	F	S
	1	2	3	4	5	6
7	8	9	10	11	12	13
14	15	16	17	18	19	20
21	22	23	24	25	26	27
28	29	30				

MAY 2013						
S	M	T	W	T	F	S
			1	2	3	4
5	6	7	8	9	10	11
12	13	14	15	16	17	18
19	20	21	22	23	24	25
26	27	28	29	30	31	

JUNE 2013						
S	M	T	W	T	F	S
						1
2	3	4	5	6	7	8
9	10	11	12	13	14	15
16	17	18	19	20	21	22
23	24	25	26	27	28	29
30						

Backyard journal

May 2013

13
Monday

14
Tuesday

15
Wednesday

16
Thursday

17
Friday

18
Saturday

Armed Forces Day

19
Sunday

Pentecost

Large, graceful
swallowtails find a home in habitats all over the world. There are more than 30 species in the U.S. and Canada, including the eastern tiger swallowtail, above. All males and many females are yellow; others are black or dark brown.

APRIL 2013						
S	M	T	W	T	F	S
	1	2	3	4	5	6
7	8	9	10	11	12	13
14	15	16	17	18	19	20
21	22	23	24	25	26	27
28	29	30				

MAY 2013						
S	M	T	W	T	F	S
			1	2	3	4
5	6	7	8	9	10	11
12	13	14	15	16	17	18
19	20	21	22	23	24	25
26	27	28	29	30	31	

JUNE 2013						
S	M	T	W	T	F	S
						1
2	3	4	5	6	7	8
9	10	11	12	13	14	15
16	17	18	19	20	21	22
23	24	25	26	27	28	29
30						

Backyard journal

May 2013

20
Monday

Victoria Day (Canada)

21
Tuesday

22
Wednesday

23
Thursday

24
Friday

25
Saturday

26
Sunday

RDA-GID

The California poppy's soft blooms almost seem to glow. Available in a rainbow of colors, these ardent self-seeders look particularly charming in a rustic setting, such as a wildflower patch or among tall grasses on a sun-drenched hillside.

APRIL 2013						
S	M	T	W	T	F	S
	1	2	3	4	5	6
7	8	9	10	11	12	13
14	15	16	17	18	19	20
21	22	23	24	25	26	27
28	29	30				

MAY 2013						
S	M	T	W	T	F	S
			1	2	3	4
5	6	7	8	9	10	11
12	13	14	15	16	17	18
19	20	21	22	23	24	25
26	27	28	29	30	31	

JUNE 2013						
S	M	T	W	T	F	S
						1
2	3	4	5	6	7	8
9	10	11	12	13	14	15
16	17	18	19	20	21	22
23	24	25	26	27	28	29
30						

June

My Garden

My garden is a lovely place
Of wonder, love and light.
And when the things of life seem wrong,
My garden turns it right.

My garden is a lovely place
Of bees and birds and blooms.
Then when my heart is full of care
I wander through its rooms.

My garden is a lovely place
In sunshine or in rain.
I listen to the raindrops fall
Upon my fair domain.

My garden is a lovely place,
I love to steal a rest.
Reposed upon my garden bench
Is where I like it best.

My garden is a lovely place,
With wondrous sights and sounds.
Lord, may my bower always be
A place where love abounds.

—CORRIE TROYER
Medina, New York

May 2013

27
Monday

Memorial Day

28
Tuesday

29
Wednesday

30
Thursday

June 2013

31
Friday

1
Saturday

2
Sunday

National Garden Week begins

West Coast
avian icons, Anna's hummingbirds like this one remain in the U.S. year-round. These flying jewels like to stay clean by bathing or preening. They'll splash around in a shallow birdbath or fly through the fine mist of a garden sprinkler.

MAY 2013						
S	M	T	W	T	F	S
			1	2	3	4
5	6	7	8	9	10	11
12	13	14	15	16	17	18
19	20	21	22	23	24	25
26	27	28	29	30	31	

JUNE 2013						
S	M	T	W	T	F	S
						1
2	3	4	5	6	7	8
9	10	11	12	13	14	15
16	17	18	19	20	21	22
23	24	25	26	27	28	29
30						

JULY 2013						
S	M	T	W	T	F	S
	1	2	3	4	5	6
7	8	9	10	11	12	13
14	15	16	17	18	19	20
21	22	23	24	25	26	27
28	29	30	31			

Backyard journal

June 2013

3
Monday

4
Tuesday

5
Wednesday

6
Thursday

7
Friday

8
Saturday

9
Sunday

Children's Sunday

Easy-care Siberian iris blossoms in richly hued flowers that look beautiful in bouquets, while the emerald-green leaves resemble long blades of grass. This garden star thrives in moist soil, ideal for the rainy days of spring and early summer.

MAY 2013						
S	M	T	W	T	F	S
			1	2	3	4
5	6	7	8	9	10	11
12	13	14	15	16	17	18
19	20	21	22	23	24	25
26	27	28	29	30	31	

JUNE 2013						
S	M	T	W	T	F	S
						1
2	3	4	5	6	7	8
9	10	11	12	13	14	15
16	17	18	19	20	21	22
23	24	25	26	27	28	29
30						

JULY 2013						
S	M	T	W	T	F	S
	1	2	3	4	5	6
7	8	9	10	11	12	13
14	15	16	17	18	19	20
21	22	23	24	25	26	27
28	29	30	31			

Backyard journal

_____
_____
_____
_____
_____
_____
_____
_____
_____
_____
_____
_____
_____
_____
_____
_____
_____
_____
_____
_____
_____
_____
_____
_____
_____
_____
_____

June 2013

10
Monday

11
Tuesday

12
Wednesday

13
Thursday

14
Friday

Flag Day

15
Saturday

16
Sunday

Father's Day

Want to spot
more butterflies, such as this Atlantis fritillary, in your garden? Winged wonders are especially drawn to purple and yellow blooms that are either daisy-shaped, like mums and cosmos, or clustered, including lantana and verbena.

MAY 2013						
S	M	T	W	T	F	S
			1	2	3	4
5	6	7	8	9	10	11
12	13	14	15	16	17	18
19	20	21	22	23	24	25
26	27	28	29	30	31	

JUNE 2013						
S	M	T	W	T	F	S
						1
2	3	4	5	6	7	8
9	10	11	12	13	14	15
16	17	18	19	20	21	22
23	24	25	26	27	28	29
30						

JULY 2013						
S	M	T	W	T	F	S
	1	2	3	4	5	6
7	8	9	10	11	12	13
14	15	16	17	18	19	20
21	22	23	24	25	26	27
28	29	30	31			

Backyard journal

17
Monday

18
Tuesday

19
Wednesday

20
Thursday

21
Friday

Summer begins

22
Saturday

23
Sunday

For millennia, lilies have captured our affection with their stunning beauty. The flowers come in numerous colors and shapes, from trumpet to bowl to recurved. If it's a sweet fragrance you desire, choose an Oriental variety.

MAY 2013

S	M	T	W	T	F	S
			1	2	3	4
5	6	7	8	9	10	11
12	13	14	15	16	17	18
19	20	21	22	23	24	25
26	27	28	29	30	31	

JUNE 2013

S	M	T	W	T	F	S
						1
2	3	4	5	6	7	8
9	10	11	12	13	14	15
16	17	18	19	20	21	22
23	24	25	26	27	28	29
30						

JULY 2013

S	M	T	W	T	F	S
	1	2	3	4	5	6
7	8	9	10	11	12	13
14	15	16	17	18	19	20
21	22	23	24	25	26	27
28	29	30	31			

Backyard journal

June 2013

24
Monday

St. Jean Baptiste Day (Canada)

25
Tuesday

26
Wednesday

27
Thursday

28
Friday

29
Saturday

30
Sunday

Persuade owls to roost in your yard by installing a wood duck house about 25 feet up on a tree trunk. Birders in the eastern U.S. or southern Canada may attract a barred owl, such as the one above, which has a distinctive "who cooks for you" call.

MAY 2013

S	M	T	W	T	F	S
			1	2	3	4
5	6	7	8	9	10	11
12	13	14	15	16	17	18
19	20	21	22	23	24	25
26	27	28	29	30	31	

JUNE 2013

S	M	T	W	T	F	S
						1
2	3	4	5	6	7	8
9	10	11	12	13	14	15
16	17	18	19	20	21	22
23	24	25	26	27	28	29
30						

JULY 2013

S	M	T	W	T	F	S
	1	2	3	4	5	6
7	8	9	10	11	12	13
14	15	16	17	18	19	20
21	22	23	24	25	26	27
28	29	30	31			

July

Butterfly

When meadows offer blossoms soft
And gentle summer breezes waft
It's then you float, as hour by hour,
You lightly dance from flower to flower.
Your life seems but a constant quest,
On fragile wings that seldom rest.
Why do you search? What lures you on?
Delays you 'til the light is gone?
Might it be nectar or perfume?
Perhaps you seek the perfect bloom.
O'er sunlit fields, on wings of gauze,
Oh, butterfly, pursue your cause.

—JUANITA FRADY WALKER
Raleigh, North Carolina

Giant swallowtail by Tom and Pat Leeson

Backyard journal

July 2013

1
Monday

Canada Day

2
Tuesday

3
Wednesday

4
Thursday

Independence Day

5
Friday

6
Saturday

7
Sunday

If you cultivate a vegetable garden, you're likely to see a black swallowtail or two fluttering nearby. Their bright green, black and yellow caterpillars use a variety of veggies and herbs as host plants, including carrots, dill, parsley and fennel.

JUNE 2013						
S	M	T	W	T	F	S
						1
2	3	4	5	6	7	8
9	10	11	12	13	14	15
16	17	18	19	20	21	22
23	24	25	26	27	28	29
30						

JULY 2013						
S	M	T	W	T	F	S
	1	2	3	4	5	6
7	8	9	10	11	12	13
14	15	16	17	18	19	20
21	22	23	24	25	26	27
28	29	30	31			

AUGUST 2013						
S	M	T	W	T	F	S
				1	2	3
4	5	6	7	8	9	10
11	12	13	14	15	16	17
18	19	20	21	22	23	24
25	26	27	28	29	30	31

Backyard journal

July 2013

8
Monday

9
Tuesday

10
Wednesday

11
Thursday

12
Friday

13
Saturday

14
Sunday

BUD HENSLEY

There's a reason you see so many photos of hummingbirds nectaring at trumpet vine: They love this sweet beauty! An eye-catching choice for a wildlife garden, it grows up to 40 feet, easily filling a trellis with its orange-red or yellow tube-shaped blossoms.

JUNE 2013

S	M	T	W	T	F	S
						1
2	3	4	5	6	7	8
9	10	11	12	13	14	15
16	17	18	19	20	21	22
23	24	25	26	27	28	29
30						

JULY 2013

S	M	T	W	T	F	S
	1	2	3	4	5	6
7	8	9	10	11	12	13
14	15	16	17	18	19	20
21	22	23	24	25	26	27
28	29	30	31			

AUGUST 2013

S	M	T	W	T	F	S
				1	2	3
4	5	6	7	8	9	10
11	12	13	14	15	16	17
18	19	20	21	22	23	24
25	26	27	28	29	30	31

Backyard journal

_____
_____
_____
_____
_____
_____
_____
_____
_____
_____
_____
_____
_____
_____
_____
_____
_____
_____
_____
_____
_____
_____
_____

July 2013

15
Monday

16
Tuesday

17
Wednesday

18
Thursday

19
Friday

20
Saturday

21
Sunday

DAWN CURRIE

Bring serenity to your yard with a water garden. Arrange a few aquatic plants in a watertight container to display on your patio or deck. Have more time on your hands? Make a big splash by installing a small pond in a garden or grassy space.

JUNE 2013						
S	M	T	W	T	F	S
						1
2	3	4	5	6	7	8
9	10	11	12	13	14	15
16	17	18	19	20	21	22
23	24	25	26	27	28	29
30						

JULY 2013						
S	M	T	W	T	F	S
	1	2	3	4	5	6
7	8	9	10	11	12	13
14	15	16	17	18	19	20
21	22	23	24	25	26	27
28	29	30	31			

AUGUST 2013						
S	M	T	W	T	F	S
				1	2	3
4	5	6	7	8	9	10
11	12	13	14	15	16	17
18	19	20	21	22	23	24
25	26	27	28	29	30	31

Backyard
journal

July 2013

22
Monday

23
Tuesday

24
Wednesday

25
Thursday

26
Friday

27
Saturday

28
Sunday

Wading through
wetlands, the great egret hunts for fish, reptiles and amphibians to spear and eat. In search of its lovely plumage, poachers threatened its survival in the early 1900s, but this graceful member of the heron family now enjoys protected status.

JUNE 2013

S	M	T	W	T	F	S
						1
2	3	4	5	6	7	8
9	10	11	12	13	14	15
16	17	18	19	20	21	22
23	24	25	26	27	28	29
30						

JULY 2013

S	M	T	W	T	F	S
	1	2	3	4	5	6
7	8	9	10	11	12	13
14	15	16	17	18	19	20
21	22	23	24	25	26	27
28	29	30	31			

AUGUST 2013

S	M	T	W	T	F	S
				1	2	3
4	5	6	7	8	9	10
11	12	13	14	15	16	17
18	19	20	21	22	23	24
25	26	27	28	29	30	31

Hummingbirds by Rolf Nussbaumer

August

On Wings of Hope

With wings spun of silver
And hearts of gold,
These tiny creatures
Our hearts behold.

Angelic features
And colors so bright
Make even the heaviest
Heart seem light.

The magical way
They flit through the sky—
They appear, then vanish
In the blink of an eye.

They're sending a message
For us to retrieve—
Anything's possible
For those who believe!

—PATTIE COPENHAVER
Tucson, Arizona

July 2013

29
Monday

30
Tuesday

31
Wednesday

1
Thursday

August 2013

2
Friday

3
Saturday

4
Sunday

Add tropical flair to your yard with lantana's colorful flower clusters. While this bird and butterfly magnet is considered a perennial only in warmer regions, folks who live in northern areas can treat lantana as an annual or bring it indoors in the winter.

RDA-GID

JULY 2013						
S	M	T	W	T	F	S
	1	2	3	4	5	6
7	8	9	10	11	12	13
14	15	16	17	18	19	20
21	22	23	24	25	26	27
28	29	30	31			

AUGUST 2013						
S	M	T	W	T	F	S
				1	2	3
4	5	6	7	8	9	10
11	12	13	14	15	16	17
18	19	20	21	22	23	24
25	26	27	28	29	30	31

SEPTEMBER 2013						
S	M	T	W	T	F	S
1	2	3	4	5	6	7
8	9	10	11	12	13	14
15	16	17	18	19	20	21
22	23	24	25	26	27	28
29	30					

August 2013

5
Monday

Civic Holiday (Canada)

6
Tuesday

7
Wednesday

8
Thursday

9
Friday

10
Saturday

11
Sunday

RDA-MKE

An entertaining
and beneficial insect, the bumble bee is a rather clumsy flier and stays on flowers, such as dahlias, bee balm and coneflowers, long enough for you to snap a photo. Don't be alarmed if you see one nearby: It only stings when threatened.

JULY 2013						
S	M	T	W	T	F	S
	1	2	3	4	5	6
7	8	9	10	11	12	13
14	15	16	17	18	19	20
21	22	23	24	25	26	27
28	29	30	31			

AUGUST 2013						
S	M	T	W	T	F	S
				1	2	3
4	5	6	7	8	9	10
11	12	13	14	15	16	17
18	19	20	21	22	23	24
25	26	27	28	29	30	31

SEPTEMBER 2013						
S	M	T	W	T	F	S
1	2	3	4	5	6	7
8	9	10	11	12	13	14
15	16	17	18	19	20	21
22	23	24	25	26	27	28
29	30					

Backyard journal

_____

_____

_____

_____

_____

_____

_____

_____

_____

_____

_____

_____

_____

_____

_____

_____

_____

_____

_____

_____

_____

_____

_____

_____

_____

_____

August 2013

12
Monday

13
Tuesday

14
Wednesday

15
Thursday

16
Friday

17
Saturday

18
Sunday

A smart landscaping pick for compact yards, ornamental mountain ash boasts masses of tiny green leaflets that turn fiery red or yellow in autumn. The red-orange or ivory berry clusters attract flocks of waxwings, catbirds, thrashers and more.

JULY 2013						
S	M	T	W	T	F	S
	1	2	3	4	5	6
7	8	9	10	11	12	13
14	15	16	17	18	19	20
21	22	23	24	25	26	27
28	29	30	31			

AUGUST 2013						
S	M	T	W	T	F	S
				1	2	3
4	5	6	7	8	9	10
11	12	13	14	15	16	17
18	19	20	21	22	23	24
25	26	27	28	29	30	31

SEPTEMBER 2013						
S	M	T	W	T	F	S
1	2	3	4	5	6	7
8	9	10	11	12	13	14
15	16	17	18	19	20	21
22	23	24	25	26	27	28
29	30					

August 2013

19
Monday

20
Tuesday

21
Wednesday

22
Thursday

23
Friday

24
Saturday

25
Sunday

Terrific in mixed flower borders or small groupings, torchlike red-hot poker plants deliver bright plumes of orange, red, yellow, white and green. For best results, well-draining soil is a must. Nectaring birds and swallowtails are sure to seek it out.

JULY 2013						
S	M	T	W	T	F	S
	1	2	3	4	5	6
7	8	9	10	11	12	13
14	15	16	17	18	19	20
21	22	23	24	25	26	27
28	29	30	31			

AUGUST 2013						
S	M	T	W	T	F	S
				1	2	3
4	5	6	7	8	9	10
11	12	13	14	15	16	17
18	19	20	21	22	23	24
25	26	27	28	29	30	31

SEPTEMBER 2013						
S	M	T	W	T	F	S
1	2	3	4	5	6	7
8	9	10	11	12	13	14
15	16	17	18	19	20	21
22	23	24	25	26	27	28
29	30					

September

Birdhouse in Sedum by Richard Day / Daybreak Imagery

Thank You, Friend

Thank you, Mother Nature
For the bounty you bestow
For seasons that delight the eye
And pleasures we all know.

The air, the soil, the water,
Lifelines for us all.
For every living creature
Whether large or small.

For each spring's awakenings
And summer's sweet delights
For autumn harvests plentiful
And winter's awesome sights.

Mother Nature's finest gift
On which we all depend
Are many of life's lessons
From our universal friend.

—PAULINE BROGNO
Sault Ste. Marie, Ontario

August 2013

26
Monday

27
Tuesday

28
Wednesday

29
Thursday

September 2013

30
Friday

31
Saturday

1
Sunday

Even though they're among the most brilliant backyard birds, North American orioles, including the Bullock's oriole here, belong to the blackbird family. As the leaves fall this season, take a walk and look for their pouchlike nests dangling in the treetops.

AUGUST 2013
S	M	T	W	T	F	S
				1	2	3
4	5	6	7	8	9	10
11	12	13	14	15	16	17
18	19	20	21	22	23	24
25	26	27	28	29	30	31

SEPTEMBER 2013
S	M	T	W	T	F	S
1	2	3	4	5	6	7
8	9	10	11	12	13	14
15	16	17	18	19	20	21
22	23	24	25	26	27	28
29	30					

OCTOBER 2013
S	M	T	W	T	F	S
		1	2	3	4	5
6	7	8	9	10	11	12
13	14	15	16	17	18	19
20	21	22	23	24	25	26
27	28	29	30	31		

Backyard journal

September 2013

2
Monday

Labor Day

3
Tuesday

4
Wednesday

Rosh Hashanah begins at sundown

5
Thursday

6
Friday

7
Saturday

8
Sunday

National Grandparents' Day

KIM CHALBECK

Include native
plants in your garden, and you're on your way to creating a small-scale wildlife habitat. Birds and butterflies, such as this cloudless sulphur, use food sources (like wild asters) that their species have depended on for generations.

AUGUST 2013						
S	M	T	W	T	F	S
				1	2	3
4	5	6	7	8	9	10
11	12	13	14	15	16	17
18	19	20	21	22	23	24
25	26	27	28	29	30	31

SEPTEMBER 2013						
S	M	T	W	T	F	S
1	2	3	4	5	6	7
8	9	10	11	12	13	14
15	16	17	18	19	20	21
22	23	24	25	26	27	28
29	30					

OCTOBER 2013						
S	M	T	W	T	F	S
		1	2	3	4	5
6	7	8	9	10	11	12
13	14	15	16	17	18	19
20	21	22	23·	24	25	26
27	28	29	30	31		

Backyard journal

September 2013

9
Monday

10
Tuesday

11
Wednesday

Patriot Day

12
Thursday

13
Friday

Yom Kippur begins at sundown

14
Saturday

15
Sunday

RICHARD CRONBERG

Fall's migration

has begun! Now's the time for birders to watch for early-flying sparrows, including the golden-crowned sparrow (above) on the West Coast. Set up a backyard stopover for migrators by providing plenty of food, water and sheltered spots.

AUGUST 2013

S	M	T	W	T	F	S
				1	2	3
4	5	6	7	8	9	10
11	12	13	14	15	16	17
18	19	20	21	22	23	24
25	26	27	28	29	30	31

SEPTEMBER 2013

S	M	T	W	T	F	S
1	2	3	4	5	6	7
8	9	10	11	12	13	14
15	16	17	18	19	20	21
22	23	24	25	26	27	28
29	30					

OCTOBER 2013

S	M	T	W	T	F	S
		1	2	3	4	5
6	7	8	9	10	11	12
13	14	15	16	17	18	19
20	21	22	23	24	25	26
27	28	29	30	31		

Backyard
journal

September 2013

16
Monday

17
Tuesday

18
Wednesday

19
Thursday

20
Friday

21
Saturday

22
Sunday

Autumn begins

TERRANOVANURSERIES.COM

Coral bells' jewel-toned foliage steals the spotlight from spring until frost; sometimes even all year-round. The mounding plants' scalloped, often mottled leaves are found in a diverse range of shades, from topaz and citrine to amethyst and onyx.

AUGUST 2013
S	M	T	W	T	F	S
				1	2	3
4	5	6	7	8	9	10
11	12	13	14	15	16	17
18	19	20	21	22	23	24
25	26	27	28	29	30	31

SEPTEMBER 2013
S	M	T	W	T	F	S
1	2	3	4	5	6	7
8	9	10	11	12	13	14
15	16	17	18	19	20	21
22	23	24	25	26	27	28
29	30					

OCTOBER 2013
S	M	T	W	T	F	S
		1	2	3	4	5
6	7	8	9	10	11	12
13	14	15	16	17	18	19
20	21	22	23	24	25	26
27	28	29	30	31		

September 2013

23
Monday

24
Tuesday

25
Wednesday

26
Thursday

27
Friday

28
Saturday

National Good Neighbor Day

29
Sunday

The mighty
monarch belongs to a small group of North American butterflies that migrate south in autumn. Millions of these fliers converge on sites in Southern California and Mexico, where they endure the winter months together.

AUGUST 2013

S	M	T	W	T	F	S
				1	2	3
4	5	6	7	8	9	10
11	12	13	14	15	16	17
18	19	20	21	22	23	24
25	26	27	28	29	30	31

SEPTEMBER 2013

S	M	T	W	T	F	S
1	2	3	4	5	6	7
8	9	10	11	12	13	14
15	16	17	18	19	20	21
22	23	24	25	26	27	28
29	30					

OCTOBER 2013

S	M	T	W	T	F	S
		1	2	3	4	5
6	7	8	9	10	11	12
13	14	15	16	17	18	19
20	21	22	23	24	25	26
27	28	29	30	31		

October

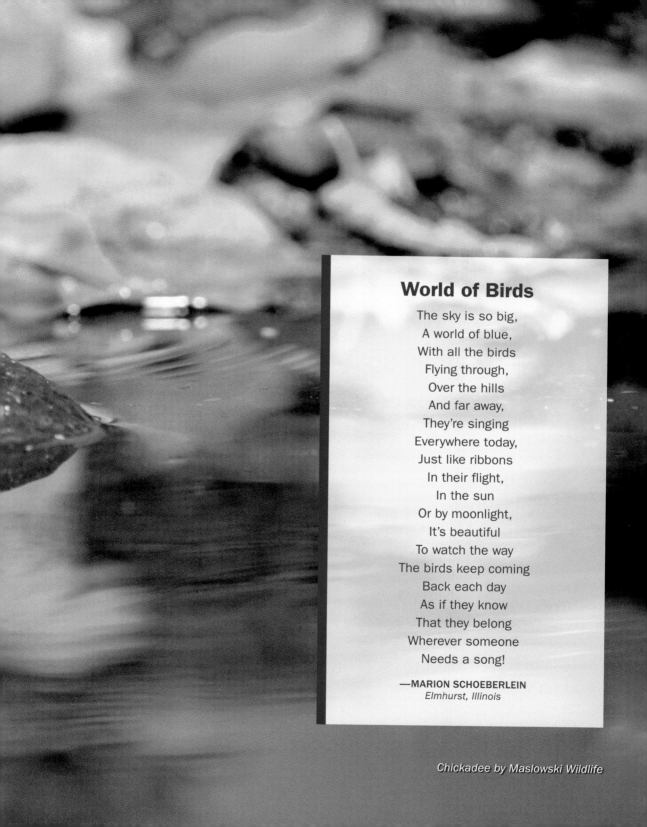

World of Birds

The sky is so big,
A world of blue,
With all the birds
Flying through,
Over the hills
And far away,
They're singing
Everywhere today,
Just like ribbons
In their flight,
In the sun
Or by moonlight,
It's beautiful
To watch the way
The birds keep coming
Back each day
As if they know
That they belong
Wherever someone
Needs a song!

—MARION SCHOEBERLEIN
Elmhurst, Illinois

Chickadee by Maslowski Wildlife

Backyard journal

September 2013

30
Monday

1
Tuesday

2
Wednesday

3
Thursday

October 2013

4
Friday

5
Saturday

6
Sunday

Now is the perfect time to start growing a majestic oak tree the old-fashioned way. Simply plant an acorn several inches deep, and protect the site to discourage critters. A white oak like the one above could eventually reach 100 feet tall!

SEPTEMBER 2013

S	M	T	W	T	F	S
1	2	3	4	5	6	7
8	9	10	11	12	13	14
15	16	17	18	19	20	21
22	23	24	25	26	27	28
29	30					

OCTOBER 2013

S	M	T	W	T	F	S
		1	2	3	4	5
6	7	8	9	10	11	12
13	14	15	16	17	18	19
20	21	22	23	24	25	26
27	28	29	30	31		

NOVEMBER 2013

S	M	T	W	T	F	S
					1	2
3	4	5	6	7	8	9
10	11	12	13	14	15	16
17	18	19	20	21	22	23
24	25	26	27	28	29	30

October 2013

7
Monday

8
Tuesday

9
Wednesday

10
Thursday

11
Friday

12
Saturday

13
Sunday

VERN LEWIS

As temperatures fall, expect these cold-lovers to drop by as they make their journey south from Alaska and the northern provinces. American tree sparrows, like this one, resemble chipping sparrows, but can be distinguished by a dark dot on the chest.

SEPTEMBER 2013						
S	M	T	W	T	F	S
1	2	3	4	5	6	7
8	9	10	11	12	13	14
15	16	17	18	19	20	21
22	23	24	25	26	27	28
29	30					

OCTOBER 2013						
S	M	T	W	T	F	S
		1	2	3	4	5
6	7	8	9	10	11	12
13	14	15	16	17	18	19
20	21	22	23	24	25	26
27	28	29	30	31		

NOVEMBER 2013						
S	M	T	W	T	F	S
					1	2
3	4	5	6	7	8	9
10	11	12	13	14	15	16
17	18	19	20	21	22	23
24	25	26	27	28	29	30

October 2013

14
Monday

Columbus Day
Thanksgiving Day (Canada)

15
Tuesday

16
Wednesday

17
Thursday

18
Friday

19
Saturday

Sweetest Day

20
Sunday

BAILEY NURSERIES

This time of year, it's difficult to miss Boston ivy, which also produces inky blue berries birds love. This brilliant climber can stretch to 50 feet long. Train yours up a wooden or chain-link fence, but beware: The tendrils can destroy brickwork.

SEPTEMBER 2013

S	M	T	W	T	F	S
1	2	3	4	5	6	7
8	9	10	11	12	13	14
15	16	17	18	19	20	21
22	23	24	25	26	27	28
29	30					

OCTOBER 2013

S	M	T	W	T	F	S
		1	2	3	4	5
6	7	8	9	10	11	12
13	14	15	16	17	18	19
20	21	22	23	24	25	26
27	28	29	30	31		

NOVEMBER 2013

S	M	T	W	T	F	S
					1	2
3	4	5	6	7	8	9
10	11	12	13	14	15	16
17	18	19	20	21	22	23
24	25	26	27	28	29	30

Backyard journal

October 2013

21
Monday

22
Tuesday

23
Wednesday

24
Thursday

25
Friday

26
Saturday

27
Sunday

A willowy, arching shrub laden with conical flower clusters, panicle hydrangea's performance is just getting started as autumn arrives. The green and yellow leaves take on hints of purple, and the creamy white blooms develop deep, blushing tones that last.

SEPTEMBER 2013

S	M	T	W	T	F	S
1	2	3	4	5	6	7
8	9	10	11	12	13	14
15	16	17	18	19	20	21
22	23	24	25	26	27	28
29	30					

OCTOBER 2013

S	M	T	W	T	F	S
		1	2	3	4	5
6	7	8	9	10	11	12
13	14	15	16	17	18	19
20	21	22	23	24	25	26
27	28	29	30	31		

NOVEMBER 2013

S	M	T	W	T	F	S
					1	2
3	4	5	6	7	8	9
10	11	12	13	14	15	16
17	18	19	20	21	22	23
24	25	26	27	28	29	30

November

November

November's gold is turning brown
And russet leaves drift slowly down
To nestle on the sun-soaked earth
And join the dust that gave them birth.

I love the autumn's mellow days
With hills obscured by smoky haze,
And dry leaves crisp beneath my feet
In country lane and city street.

The maple's garb of flaming red
And gray geese honking overhead
Proclaim November's swift retreat
And mark the passage of her feet.

—ANETA KENNY
Brandon, Manitoba

Frog by T. Gainey / GAP Photos Ltd.

Backyard journal

October 2013

28
Monday

29
Tuesday

30
Wednesday

31
Thursday

Halloween

November 2013

1
Friday

All Saints Day

2
Saturday

3
Sunday

Daylight Saving Time ends

While all other birds climb upward in search of food, quirky nuthatches (including the white-breasted species above) do exactly the opposite. They frequent feeders, but their natural diet includes berries, nuts and seeds, as well as insects.

OCTOBER 2013						
S	M	T	W	T	F	S
		1	2	3	4	5
6	7	8	9	10	11	12
13	14	15	16	17	18	19
20	21	22	23	24	25	26
27	28	29	30	31		

NOVEMBER 2013						
S	M	T	W	T	F	S
					1	2
3	4	5	6	7	8	9
10	11	12	13	14	15	16
17	18	19	20	21	22	23
24	25	26	27	28	29	30

DECEMBER 2013						
S	M	T	W	T	F	S
1	2	3	4	5	6	7
8	9	10	11	12	13	14
15	16	17	18	19	20	21
22	23	24	25	26	27	28
29	30	31				

November 2013

4
Monday

5
Tuesday

Election Day

6
Wednesday

7
Thursday

8
Friday

9
Saturday

10
Sunday

Blushing red
cool-season foliage and unique, yellow-green spring flowers give wood spurge long-term landscape appeal. Keep this branching evergreen perennial in shape by deadheading. But wear gloves when doing so— it's poisonous.

OCTOBER 2013

S	M	T	W	T	F	S
		1	2	3	4	5
6	7	8	9	10	11	12
13	14	15	16	17	18	19
20	21	22	23	24	25	26
27	28	29	30	31		

NOVEMBER 2013

S	M	T	W	T	F	S
					1	2
3	4	5	6	7	8	9
10	11	12	13	14	15	16
17	18	19	20	21	22	23
24	25	26	27	28	29	30

DECEMBER 2013

S	M	T	W	T	F	S
1	2	3	4	5	6	7
8	9	10	11	12	13	14
15	16	17	18	19	20	21
22	23	24	25	26	27	28
29	30	31				

Backyard journal

November 2013

11
Monday

Veterans Day
Remembrance Day (Canada)

12
Tuesday

13
Wednesday

14
Thursday

15
Friday

16
Saturday

17
Sunday

Feeder visitors
tend to be much smaller,
but Cooper's hawks also
glide into backyards
looking for food—
typically mid-sized birds,
such as pigeons and
starlings. It never hurts
to plant protective trees
and shrubs to help keep
songbirds safe.

OCTOBER 2013

S	M	T	W	T	F	S
		1	2	3	4	5
6	7	8	9	10	11	12
13	14	15	16	17	18	19
20	21	22	23	24	25	26
27	28	29	30	31		

NOVEMBER 2013

S	M	T	W	T	F	S
					1	2
3	4	5	6	7	8	9
10	11	12	13	14	15	16
17	18	19	20	21	22	23
24	25	26	27	28	29	30

DECEMBER 2013

S	M	T	W	T	F	S
1	2	3	4	5	6	7
8	9	10	11	12	13	14
15	16	17	18	19	20	21
22	23	24	25	26	27	28
29	30	31				

Backyard
journal

November 2013

18
Monday

19
Tuesday

20
Wednesday

21
Thursday

22
Friday

23
Saturday

24
Sunday

Showy, orange berries that dangle from American bittersweet are a favorite of more than a dozen American bird species. Growing up to 30 feet tall, it offers ample shelter. Choose this native species over its invasive cousin, Oriental bittersweet.

OCTOBER 2013

S	M	T	W	T	F	S
		1	2	3	4	5
6	7	8	9	10	11	12
13	14	15	16	17	18	19
20	21	22	23	24	25	26
27	28	29	30	31		

NOVEMBER 2013

S	M	T	W	T	F	S
					1	2
3	4	5	6	7	8	9
10	11	12	13	14	15	16
17	18	19	20	21	22	23
24	25	26	27	28	29	30

DECEMBER 2013

S	M	T	W	T	F	S
1	2	3	4	5	6	7
8	9	10	11	12	13	14
15	16	17	18	19	20	21
22	23	24	25	26	27	28
29	30	31				

December

Out My Window

I looked out my window to a glorious sight.
Everything was covered in a blanket white!
Snow fell for many hours during the night;
And, when the sun arose, all looked bright.

Now the snow rested on limbs of the tree.
Some cardinals sat there singing for me;
Along came a nuthatch, flying so free.
Soon they were joined by a chickadee.

The feeders were busy; it was cold outside.
But the birds kept alert with eyes open wide.
The local hawk hunts…oh, yes, he has tried
To catch songbirds feeding with awareness aside.

From gloom of gray days, snow was a break,
I enjoyed the splendid view for beauty's sake.
From my window, a snapshot I decided to take
Capturing the lovely scene that snow can make.

—SHARON MILLER BOLANDER
Flushing, Michigan

Blue jay and northern cardinal by Maslowski Wildlife

Backyard
journal

_____

_____

_____

_____

_____

_____

_____

_____

_____

_____

_____

_____

_____

_____

_____

_____

_____

_____

_____

_____

_____

_____

November 2013

25
Monday

26
Tuesday

27
Wednesday

Hanukkah begins at sundown

28
Thursday

Thanksgiving Day

December 2013

29
Friday

30
Saturday

1
Sunday

Advent begins

DONNIS MORGAN

Black-capped chickadees take the backyard prize for most entertaining. When these vivacious birds get together, they're full of cheerful conversation. They're also remarkably tame, known to perch on an outstretched hand to feast on seed.

NOVEMBER 2013						
S	M	T	W	T	F	S
					1	2
3	4	5	6	7	8	9
10	11	12	13	14	15	16
17	18	19	20	21	22	23
24	25	26	27	28	29	30

DECEMBER 2013						
S	M	T	W	T	F	S
1	2	3	4	5	6	7
8	9	10	11	12	13	14
15	16	17	18	19	20	21
22	23	24	25	26	27	28
29	30	31				

JANUARY 2014						
S	M	T	W	T	F	S
			1	2	3	4
5	6	7	8	9	10	11
12	13	14	15	16	17	18
19	20	21	22	23	24	25
26	27	28	29	30	31	

Backyard journal

_____

_____

_____

_____

_____

_____

_____

_____

_____

_____

_____

_____

_____

_____

_____

_____

_____

_____

_____

_____

_____

_____

_____

_____

_____

December 2013

2
Monday

3
Tuesday

4
Wednesday

5
Thursday

6
Friday

St. Nicholas' Day

7
Saturday

8
Sunday

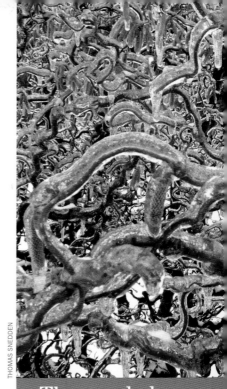

THOMAS SNEDDEN

The gnarled, asymmetrical silhouette of Harry Lauder's walking stick will add a distinctive touch in every season, with its curled branches and fluttering, wrinkled leaves. Have a small space? This shrub is able to thrive in a container as well.

NOVEMBER 2013

S	M	T	W	T	F	S
					1	2
3	4	5	6	7	8	9
10	11	12	13	14	15	16
17	18	19	20	21	22	23
24	25	26	27	28	29	30

DECEMBER 2013

S	M	T	W	T	F	S
1	2	3	4	5	6	7
8	9	10	11	12	13	14
15	16	17	18	19	20	21
22	23	24	25	26	27	28
29	30	31				

JANUARY 2014

S	M	T	W	T	F	S
			1	2	3	4
5	6	7	8	9	10	11
12	13	14	15	16	17	18
19	20	21	22	23	24	25
26	27	28	29	30	31	

December 2013

9
Monday

10
Tuesday

11
Wednesday

12
Thursday

13
Friday

14
Saturday

15
Sunday

You'll entice many fliers with birdseed and suet, but you can attract other species, like cedar waxwings, by landscaping with berry-bearing plants. They'll first grace your yard with branches of blooms, then they produce fruit later in the year.

NOVEMBER 2013

S	M	T	W	T	F	S
					1	2
3	4	5	6	7	8	9
10	11	12	13	14	15	16
17	18	19	20	21	22	23
24	25	26	27	28	29	30

DECEMBER 2013

S	M	T	W	T	F	S
1	2	3	4	5	6	7
8	9	10	11	12	13	14
15	16	17	18	19	20	21
22	23	24	25	26	27	28
29	30	31				

JANUARY 2014

S	M	T	W	T	F	S
			1	2	3	4
5	6	7	8	9	10	11
12	13	14	15	16	17	18
19	20	21	22	23	24	25
26	27	28	29	30	31	

December 2013

16
Monday

17
Tuesday

18
Wednesday

19
Thursday

20
Friday

21
Saturday

Winter begins

22
Sunday

A poinsettia's true beauty is not in the flower, but rather in the bracts: The large, sun-loving leaves at the base of the tiny flower turn from green into more vibrant colors. Once found only in red, they are now bred in white, pink and yellow, too.

NOVEMBER 2013						
S	M	T	W	T	F	S
					1	2
3	4	5	6	7	8	9
10	11	12	13	14	15	16
17	18	19	20	21	22	23
24	25	26	27	28	29	30

DECEMBER 2013						
S	M	T	W	T	F	S
1	2	3	4	5	6	7
8	9	10	11	12	13	14
15	16	17	18	19	20	21
22	23	24	25	26	27	28
29	30	31				

JANUARY 2014						
S	M	T	W	T	F	S
			1	2	3	4
5	6	7	8	9	10	11
12	13	14	15	16	17	18
19	20	21	22	23	24	25
26	27	28	29	30	31	

December 2013

23
Monday

24
Tuesday

Christmas Eve

25
Wednesday

Christmas Day

26
Thursday

Boxing Day (Canada)

27
Friday

28
Saturday

29
Sunday

Give a nod to the holiday season with festive blue holly. Boasting red berries, showy purple stems and evergreen bluish or multicolored leaves, this bushy, resilient plant comes in a wide range of sizes, so it's ideal for any size yard.

NOVEMBER 2013

S	M	T	W	T	F	S
					1	2
3	4	5	6	7	8	9
10	11	12	13	14	15	16
17	18	19	20	21	22	23
24	25	26	27	28	29	30

DECEMBER 2013

S	M	T	W	T	F	S
1	2	3	4	5	6	7
8	9	10	11	12	13	14
15	16	17	18	19	20	21
22	23	24	25	26	27	28
29	30	31				

JANUARY 2014

S	M	T	W	T	F	S
			1	2	3	4
5	6	7	8	9	10	11
12	13	14	15	16	17	18
19	20	21	22	23	24	25
26	27	28	29	30	31	

December 2013

30
Monday

31
Tuesday

New Year's Eve

1
Wednesday

New Year's Day

2
Thursday

January 2014

3
Friday

4
Saturday

5
Sunday

In winter, no matter if your yard is snowy or drab, this bird's scarlet noggin will catch your eye. The red-headed woodpecker stockpiles food, including nuts, insects and berries. You'll likely spot them at feeders, too, eating suet or sunflower seeds.

NOVEMBER 2013

S	M	T	W	T	F	S
					1	2
3	4	5	6	7	8	9
10	11	12	13	14	15	16
17	18	19	20	21	22	23
24	25	26	27	28	29	30

DECEMBER 2013

S	M	T	W	T	F	S
1	2	3	4	5	6	7
8	9	10	11	12	13	14
15	16	17	18	19	20	21
22	23	24	25	26	27	28
29	30	31				

JANUARY 2014

S	M	T	W	T	F	S
			1	2	3	4
5	6	7	8	9	10	11
12	13	14	15	16	17	18
19	20	21	22	23	24	25
26	27	28	29	30	31	

2014 Monthly Planner

JANUARY 2014

S	M	T	W	T	F	S
			1	2	3	4
5	6	7	8	9	10	11
12	13	14	15	16	17	18
19	20	21	22	23	24	25
26	27	28	29	30	31	

FEBRUARY 2014

S	M	T	W	T	F	S
						1
2	3	4	5	6	7	8
9	10	11	12	13	14	15
16	17	18	19	20	21	22
23	24	25	26	27	28	

MARCH 2014

S	M	T	W	T	F	S
						1
2	3	4	5	6	7	8
9	10	11	12	13	14	15
16	17	18	19	20	21	22
23	24	25	26	27	28	29
30	31					

APRIL 2014

S	M	T	W	T	F	S
		1	2	3	4	5
6	7	8	9	10	11	12
13	14	15	16	17	18	19
20	21	22	23	24	25	26
27	28	29	30			

MAY 2014

S	M	T	W	T	F	S
				1	2	3
4	5	6	7	8	9	10
11	12	13	14	15	16	17
18	19	20	21	22	23	24
25	26	27	28	29	30	31

JUNE 2014

S	M	T	W	T	F	S
1	2	3	4	5	6	7
8	9	10	11	12	13	14
15	16	17	18	19	20	21
22	23	24	25	26	27	28
29	30					

JULY 2014

S	M	T	W	T	F	S
		1	2	3	4	5
6	7	8	9	10	11	12
13	14	15	16	17	18	19
20	21	22	23	24	25	26
27	28	29	30	31		

AUGUST 2014

S	M	T	W	T	F	S
					1	2
3	4	5	6	7	8	9
10	11	12	13	14	15	16
17	18	19	20	21	22	23
24	25	26	27	28	29	30
31						

SEPTEMBER 2014

S	M	T	W	T	F	S
	1	2	3	4	5	6
7	8	9	10	11	12	13
14	15	16	17	18	19	20
21	22	23	24	25	26	27
28	29	30				

OCTOBER 2014

S	M	T	W	T	F	S
			1	2	3	4
5	6	7	8	9	10	11
12	13	14	15	16	17	18
19	20	21	22	23	24	25
26	27	28	29	30	31	

NOVEMBER 2014

S	M	T	W	T	F	S
						1
2	3	4	5	6	7	8
9	10	11	12	13	14	15
16	17	18	19	20	21	22
23	24	25	26	27	28	29
30						

DECEMBER 2014

S	M	T	W	T	F	S
	1	2	3	4	5	6
7	8	9	10	11	12	13
14	15	16	17	18	19	20
21	22	23	24	25	26	27
28	29	30	31			

January

April

February

March

May

June

JANUARY 2014

S	M	T	W	T	F	S
			1	2	3	4
5	6	7	8	9	10	11
12	13	14	15	16	17	18
19	20	21	22	23	24	25
26	27	28	29	30	31	

FEBRUARY 2014

S	M	T	W	T	F	S
						1
2	3	4	5	6	7	8
9	10	11	12	13	14	15
16	17	18	19	20	21	22
23	24	25	26	27	28	

MARCH 2014

S	M	T	W	T	F	S
						1
2	3	4	5	6	7	8
9	10	11	12	13	14	15
16	17	18	19	20	21	22
23	24	25	26	27	28	29
30	31					

APRIL 2014

S	M	T	W	T	F	S
		1	2	3	4	5
6	7	8	9	10	11	12
13	14	15	16	17	18	19
20	21	22	23	24	25	26
27	28	29	30			

MAY 2014

S	M	T	W	T	F	S
				1	2	3
4	5	6	7	8	9	10
11	12	13	14	15	16	17
18	19	20	21	22	23	24
25	26	27	28	29	30	31

JUNE 2014

S	M	T	W	T	F	S
1	2	3	4	5	6	7
8	9	10	11	12	13	14
15	16	17	18	19	20	21
22	23	24	25	26	27	28
29	30					

JULY 2014

S	M	T	W	T	F	S
		1	2	3	4	5
6	7	8	9	10	11	12
13	14	15	16	17	18	19
20	21	22	23	24	25	26
27	28	29	30	31		

AUGUST 2014

S	M	T	W	T	F	S
					1	2
3	4	5	6	7	8	9
10	11	12	13	14	15	16
17	18	19	20	21	22	23
24	25	26	27	28	29	30
31						

SEPTEMBER 2014

S	M	T	W	T	F	S
	1	2	3	4	5	6
7	8	9	10	11	12	13
14	15	16	17	18	19	20
21	22	23	24	25	26	27
28	29	30				

OCTOBER 2014

S	M	T	W	T	F	S
			1	2	3	4
5	6	7	8	9	10	11
12	13	14	15	16	17	18
19	20	21	22	23	24	25
26	27	28	29	30	31	

NOVEMBER 2014

S	M	T	W	T	F	S
						1
2	3	4	5	6	7	8
9	10	11	12	13	14	15
16	17	18	19	20	21	22
23	24	25	26	27	28	29
30						

DECEMBER 2014

S	M	T	W	T	F	S
	1	2	3	4	5	6
7	8	9	10	11	12	13
14	15	16	17	18	19	20
21	22	23	24	25	26	27
28	29	30	31			

July

October

August

September

November

December

Birds in Your Region

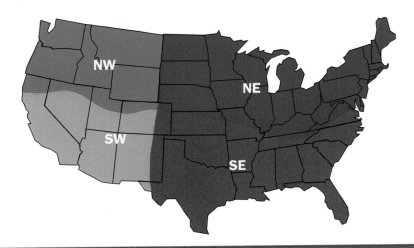

BIRD	SUMMER					WINTER			
	NE	NW	SE	SW		NE	NW	SE	SW
BLACKBIRDS									
Brewer's blackbird		●					●	●	●
Brown-headed cowbird	●	●	●	●		●		●	●
Common grackle	●		●					●	
Red-winged blackbird	●	●	●	●		●	●	●	●
BLUEBIRDS									
Eastern bluebird	●		●			●		●	
Mountain bluebird		●		●					●
Western bluebird		●	●				●		●
BUNTINGS									
Indigo bunting	●		●						
Lazuli bunting		●							
Painted bunting			●					●	
BUSHTIT									
Bushtit		●		●			●		●
CARDINAL									
Northern cardinal	●		●	●		●		●	●
CHICKADEES									
Black-capped chickadee	●	●				●	●		
Carolina chickadee			●					●	
Mountain chickadee		●		●			●		●

BIRD	SUMMER					WINTER				
	NE	NW	SE	SW		NE	NW	SE	SW	
CREEPER										
Brown creeper	●	●		●		●	●	●	●	
CROSSBILL										
Red crossbill	●	●		●		●	●		●	
FINCHES										
American goldfinch	●	●	●			●	●	●	●	
Common redpoll						●	●			
House finch	●	●	●	●		●	●	●	●	
Pine siskin		●		●		●	●	●	●	
Purple finch	●	●				●	●	●	●	
GROSBEAKS										
Black-headed grosbeak		●		●						
Blue grosbeak			●	●						
Evening grosbeak	●	●		●		●	●	●	●	
Pine grosbeak		●				●	●			
HUMMINGBIRDS										
Anna's hummingbird		●		●			●		●	
Black-chinned hummingbird		●		●						
Broad-tailed hummingbird				●						
Calliope hummingbird		●								
Ruby-throated hummingbird	●		●							
Rufous hummingbird		●								
JAYS										
Blue jay	●		●			●		●		
Gray jay		●								
Pinyon jay		●		●			●		●	
Scrub jay		●		●			●		●	
Steller's jay		●		●			●		●	
JUNCO										
Dark-eyed junco	●	●		●		●	●	●	●	
KINGLETS										
Golden-crowned kinglet		●		●		●	●	●	●	
Ruby-crowned kinglet		●				●	●	●	●	
MIMIC THRUSHES										
Brown thrasher	●		●					●		
Gray catbird	●	●	●					●		
Northern mockingbird	●		●	●		●		●	●	

Birds in Your Region

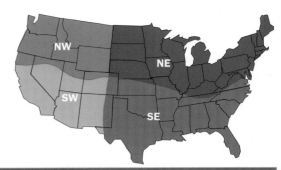

(continued)

BIRD	SUMMER					WINTER			
	NE	NW	SE	SW		NE	NW	SE	SW
NUTHATCHES									
Brown-headed nuthatch			•					•	
Pygmy nuthatch		•		•			•		•
Red-breasted nuthatch	•	•		•		•	•	•	•
White-breasted nuthatch	•	•	•	•		•	•	•	•
ORIOLES									
Baltimore oriole	•		•					•	
Bullock's oriole		•		•					•
Orchard oriole	•		•						
Scott's oriole				•					
PIGEONS									
Mourning dove	•	•	•	•		•	•	•	•
Rock dove	•	•	•	•		•	•	•	•
SPARROWS									
American tree sparrow						•	•		
Chipping sparrow	•	•	•	•				•	•
Field sparrow	•		•					•	
Fox sparrow		•						•	•
House sparrow	•	•	•	•		•	•	•	•
Song sparrow	•	•	•	•		•	•	•	•
Swamp sparrow	•					•		•	
White-crowned sparrow		•						•	•
White-throated sparrow	•							•	•
STARLING									
European starling	•	•	•	•		•	•	•	•
TANAGERS									
Scarlet tanager	•								
Summer tanager			•	•					
Western tanager		•		•					
THRUSHES									
American robin	•	•	•	•			•	•	•
Hermit thrush	•	•		•				•	•
Wood thrush	•		•						

BIRD	SUMMER					WINTER			
	NE	NW	SE	SW		NE	NW	SE	SW
TITMICE									
Plain titmouse				●					●
Tufted titmouse	●		●			●		●	
TOWHEES									
Eastern towhee	●		●			●		●	
Spotted towhee		●		●			●		●
VIREOS									
Red-eyed vireo	●	●	●						
Warbling vireo	●	●	●	●					
White-eyed vireo			●					●	
WARBLERS									
American redstart	●	●	●						
Black and white warbler	●		●						
Black-throated blue warbler	●								
Common yellowthroat	●	●	●	●				●	
Hooded warbler			●						
Ovenbird	●	●							
Wilson's warbler	●	●							
Yellow warbler	●	●	●	●					
Yellow-rumped warbler	●	●					●	●	●
WAXWINGS									
Bohemian waxwing							●		
Cedar waxwing	●	●						●	●
WOODPECKERS									
Downy woodpecker	●	●	●	●		●	●	●	●
Gilded flicker				●					●
Hairy woodpecker	●	●	●	●		●	●	●	●
Ladder-backed woodpecker				●					●
Lewis woodpecker		●		●			●		●
Northern flicker	●	●	●	●		●	●	●	●
Red-bellied woodpecker	●		●			●		●	
Red-breasted sapsucker		●					●		●
Red-headed woodpecker	●		●			●		●	
Yellow-bellied sapsucker	●		●					●	●
WRENS									
Cactus wren				●				●	
Carolina wren	●		●			●		●	
House wren	●	●	●	●				●	●
Winter wren	●	●						●	●

Birds I Saw This Year

Species	M / F	Date	Observations

Species	M / F	Date	Observations

Birds and Their Favorite Foods

	Nyjer (thistle) seed	Cracked corn	White proso millet	Black-oil sunflower seed	Hulled sunflower seed	Beef suet	Fruit	Sugar water/ nectar*
Rose-breasted grosbeak				●	●			
Black-headed grosbeak				●	●			
Evening grosbeak		●	●	●	●			
Northern cardinal		●	●	●	●		●	
Indigo bunting	●				●			
Eastern towhee	●	●	●	●	●			
Dark-eyed junco	●	●	●	●	●			
White-crowned sparrow	●	●	●	●	●			
White-throated sparrow	●	●	●	●	●			
American tree sparrow	●	●	●	●	●			
Chipping sparrow	●	●	●	●	●			
Song sparrow	●	●	●	●	●			
House sparrow	●	●	●	●	●			
House finch	●	●	●	●	●			
Purple finch	●	●	●	●	●			
American goldfinch	●	●	●	●	●			
Pine siskin	●	●	●	●	●			
Scarlet tanager							●	●
Western tanager							●	●
Baltimore oriole							●	●
Red-winged blackbird		●		●	●			
Eastern bluebird							●	
Wood thrush							●	
American robin							●	
Gray catbird							●	
Northern mockingbird							●	
Brown thrasher							●	
Ruby-throated hummingbird								●
Anna's hummingbird								●
Broad-tailed hummingbird								●
Tufted titmouse	●			●	●	●		
Black-capped chickadee	●			●	●	●		
White-breasted nuthatch				●	●	●		
Carolina wren						●		
Cedar waxwing							●	
Woodpecker				●	●	●	●	
Scrub jay		●		●	●	●	●	
Blue jay		●		●	●	●	●	
Mourning dove	●	●	●	●	●			
Northern bobwhite		●	●		●			
Ring-necked pheasant		●	●		●			
Canada goose		●						
Mallard		●						

* To make sugar water for hummingbirds, mix 4 parts water with 1 part sugar.
Boil, cool and serve. Store leftovers in the refrigerator for up to a week. Change feeder nectar every three to five days.

Source: *Garden Birds of America* by George H. Harrison. Willow Creek Press, 1996.

Birdhouse Building Guidelines

SPECIES	DIMENSIONS	HOLE	PLACEMENT	COLOR	NOTES
Eastern bluebird	5" x 5" x 8"h.	1½" centered 6" above floor	5-10' high in the open; sunny area	light earth tones	likes open areas, especially facing a field
Tree swallow	5" x 5" x 6"h.	1½" centered 4" above floor	5-8' high in the open; 50-100% sun	light earth tones or gray	within 2 miles of pond or lake
Purple martin	multiple apts. 6" x 6" x 6" ea.	2½" hole 2¼" above floor	15-20' high in the open	white	open yard without tall trees; near water
Tufted titmouse	4" x 4" x 8"h.	1¼"	4-10' high	light earth tones	prefers to live in or near woods
Chickadee	4" x 4" x 8"h. or 5" x 5" base	1⅛" centered 6" above floor	4-8' high	light earth tones	small tree thicket
Nuthatch	4" x 4" x 10"h.	1¼" centered 7½" above floor	12-25' high on tree trunk	bark-covered or natural	
House wren	4" x 4" x 8"h. or 4" x 6" base	1" centered 6" above floor	5-10' high on post or hung in tree	light earth tones or white	may fill nest boxes with "dummy" nests
Northern flicker	7" x 7" x 18"h.	2½" centered 14" above floor	8-20' high	light earth tones	put 4" sawdust inside for nesting
Downy woodpecker	4" x 4" x 10"h.	1¼" centered 7½" above floor	12-25' high on tree trunk	simulate natural cavity	prefers own excavation; provide sawdust
Red-headed woodpecker	6" x 6" x 15"h.	2" centered 6-8" above floor	8-20' high on post or tree trunk	simulate natural cavity	needs sawdust for nesting
Wood duck	10" x 10" x 24"h.	4" x 3" elliptical 20" above floor	2-5' high on post over water, or 12-40' high on tree facing water	light earth tones or natural	needs 3-4" of sawdust or shavings for nesting
American kestrel	10" x 10" x 24"h.	4" x 3" elliptical 20" above floor	12-40' high on post or tree trunk	light earth tones or natural	needs open approach on edge of woodlot or in isolated tree
Screech-owl	10" x 10" x 24"h.	4" x 3" elliptical 20" above floor	2-5' high on post over water, or 12-40' high on tree	light earth tones or natural	prefers open woods or edge of woodlot
NESTING SHELVES					
American robin	6" x 6" x 8"h.	none—needs roof for rain protection	on side of building or arbor or in tree	light earth tones or wood	use is irregular
Barn swallow	6" x 6" x 8"h.	none—does not need roof	under eaves of building	light earth tones or wood	prefers barns or outbuildings
Phoebe	6" x 6" x 8"h.	none—does not need roof	under eaves of building	light earth tones or wood	prefers water nearby

Note: With the exception of wrens, birds do not tolerate swaying birdhouses. Birdhouses should be firmly anchored to a post, a tree or the side of a building.

Source: *Garden Birds of America* by George H. Harrison. Willow Creek Press, 1996.

beauty in all
seasons

Follow these tips for an eye-catching backyard all year long.

BY MELINDA MYERS

Don't turn the page. I'm talking about more than evergreens during the winter. And that goes for those of you who live in the far North as well as the South.

I admit the Northern winter garden has a different look than one in Florida or the Southwest. But some of the joy—and the challenge—of gardening lies in the diversity of our landscapes. Here are some things to consider for a year-round landscaping plan.

A good rule of thumb is to look for plants with interesting forms. The spreading branches of a redbud or pagoda dogwood are dramatic whether blooming, flaunting fall color or displaying their stark winter shapes. Weeping forms of crabapple, katsura and other landscape trees are also great year-round.

Plants with Seasonal Sizzle

The multicolored bark of crape myrtle is appealing in every season. Northern gardeners can try paper and river birch for a similar effect. And don't forget about shrubs like the colorful yellowtwig and redtwig dogwoods (top right), bright green stems of kerria and the exfoliating bark of oakleaf hydrangea, ninebark and the climbing hydrangea vine.

Flowers and fruit add seasonal punch, and many plants provide both. Disease-resistant crabapples (such as the ones on the lower right) with small, persistent fruit are great four-season plants.

The serviceberry is another favorite, with handsome fall color, smooth gray bark and edible fruit following the spring flowers. Though the blueberry-like fruits last only weeks, the birds love them.

Shrubs like witch hazel and its relative fothergilla are other good choices. The common witch hazel blooms in fall, when most plants are starting to shut down; the vernal

witch hazel blossoms in late winter or early spring. Fothergilla has fragrant white flowers in spring and lovely foliage in fall.

You might even consider adding a few viburnums to your yard. Some are evergreen in the Midwest and South; most have pretty and sometimes fragrant blooms, brightly colored fruit and lovely fall color.

Perennial Mainstays

Count on perennials. Ornamental grasses lend motion and texture through much of the year; the foliage, flowers and interesting seed heads that persist through winter provide your landscape an ever-changing display.

Two-row stonecrop, evening primrose, willow amsonia, balloon flower, hosta and many perennial geraniums boast eye-catching fall color. Coral bells, yucca and bergenia have nice foliage in autumn and winter in many areas.

And of course, be sure to add a few evergreens. The hardy greenery creates a good backdrop for your ornamental grasses, perennials and deciduous trees and shrubs. Those with striking color, form or texture provide a focal point in the garden. Evergreens are available in almost every size and shape, so it's not difficult to find a few that will complement your landscape.

WHY
feed birds?

Frequent *Birds & Blooms* contributors
share why they feed feathered friends.

BY DAVID SHAW

To the uninitiated, birding and bird feeding might seem like an absurd waste of time, money and energy.

From a practical standpoint, my passion for birds does seem a bit silly. I go to extraordinary lengths to watch, feed, photograph and be in the presence of these wonderful winged creatures. So every once in awhile, I've found myself considering this question—why?

I once had a college professor who provided me with some insight into this passion. I remember talking to him as he admired a flock of 10,000 western sandpipers swirling in the air. As he stared upward at the moving mass of birds, he said, "Every western sandpiper in the world could go extinct tomorrow, and we would feel no economic impact of that loss. But what would be lost is beauty."

Conservationists are constantly trying to put the importance of wildlife, wilderness and nature into economic terms. As though the dollar value of a flock of shorebirds or the birds at my feeders is the only thing that matters.

This, I now realize, is utter nonsense. What makes birds valuable, what makes them worthy of our protection, is their inherent beauty. It is their beauty that enriches our lives, not their economic value. And this enrichment is priceless.

In this age, the noise of televisions, computers, the Internet and vehicles constantly surrounds us. Buried in this cacophony of multimedia, we are far removed from the natural world. Yet part of me yearns for that connection.

Our genetic history is tied to natural wildness, and in its absence, there is a loss. Birds are my solution.

I can admire migrant songbirds moving through city parks, and finches, robins and blackbirds in suburban backyards.

Birds are everywhere. Yet no matter how familiar they may be, they are subjected to wind, rain, snow, cold, predators and the trials of migration. Hold no doubt, birds are wild animals, and through them we can regain a thread of connection to their wildness.

Therein lies the answer to why I participate in this seemingly pointless activity. It is part of a struggle to maintain a connection to the wild.

I invite these small, feathered, wild things into my yard and into my life with feeders of seed. I wander into the birds' realm—forests, beaches, mountains and wetlands— to experience their beauty on their own terms.

These explorations restore balance to my life, and finding that balance is more reason than I need to justify my passion for birds.

Songbirds bring an added dimension of attraction with their variety of colors, patterns, continual motion and melodic songs. Besides, having birds in my garden simply makes me happy! **—KRIS WETHERBEE**
Oakland, Oregon

I feed birds because it is in my DNA. My father, Hal Harrison, made his living as a nature journalist and public speaker primarily about birds. I, too, have made it a career, focusing on getting people involved in feeding birds for the joy of it and as a way to become part of nature. **—GEORGE HARRISON**
Hubertus, Wisconsin

The biggest reason I feed the birds is that I just thoroughly enjoy watching them fly to the feeders, eat a little, fly away and then come back for more. It gives me so much pleasure that I smile as write this!
—LAURA CARTWRIGHT
Booneville, Mississippi

Feeding my feathered friends makes it easy for me to study their fascinating behavior and admire their beauty, even as I work at my desk! And these days, when wildlife is in such worldwide peril, I enjoy giving birds a helping hand, especially during harsh winters.

—NATALIE ROWE
Apple Hill, Ontario

winter

Winter is an ideal time to feed the birds and look ahead to the upcoming season. Use these colder months for spring planning and cleanup.

- **PAINT OR REPAIR** any birdhouses that need fixing up. Or build new ones altogether.

- **INVENTORY YOUR CONTAINERS,** including saucers. Discard worn or cracked pieces and clean the rest, inside and out. Rinse in a 10-percent bleach-to-water solution to kill diseases or pests.

- **MAKE A BIRD WREATH** to hang outside and decorate it with your visitors' favorite foods.

- **PRUNE AWAY BRANCHES** with overwintering egg masses left by tree pests. Doing so will eliminate much of the problem for the upcoming growing season.

- **START A BIRD JOURNAL** to keep track of all the different species you see as the new year begins.

- **PLAN FOR YOUR SPRING GARDEN.** Determine which birds and butterflies you can attract, and make a list of the plants you will need. Look up caterpillar host plants, too.

- **PREVENT WINTER DAMAGE** to your evergreen trees, hedges and shrubs. Wrap hedges with landscape netting and loosely tie branches of upright evergreens with cloth strips. This prevents snow from weighing down limbs and breaking branches.

- **WAIT UNTIL THE GROUND FREEZES** to apply winter mulch. Applying it any earlier provides habitat for plant-eating animals and encourages disease.

spring

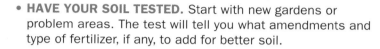

With the spring season comes many backyard tasks. There is a lot to do, but take it slow and prioritize! Both flora and fauna will appreciate your thought-out plan to make your backyard its best.

- **HAVE YOUR SOIL TESTED.** Start with new gardens or problem areas. The test will tell you what amendments and type of fertilizer, if any, to add for better soil.

- **RESTART BIRDBATH AND POND OPERATIONS.** Water is very popular in spring as migrants pass through. And it's a great way to attract new winged visitors!

- **ATTACK WEEDS EARLY,** before they develop big root systems or go to seed. They're easier to yank out or knock down (with a sharp hoe) after a rain or good watering.

- **PRUNE AND SHAPE SPRING-FLOWERING SHRUBS** after their show is over. If you wait too long, you may chop off next year's buds.

- **INSTALL A RAIN BARREL** where it won't be in the way or be obstructed by branches or leaves. Cover it with a screen to keep out debris and bugs.

- **WATCH FOR THE FIRST MIGRANT BIRDS** of spring, including red-winged blackbirds, American robins, phoebes, warblers and tree swallows.

- **CHECK SPRING FLOWERS,** such as violas and creeping phlox, for newly emerged nectaring butterflies, such as cabbage whites, blues and sulphurs.

- **FILL BIRD FEEDERS DAILY.** Natural food is in short supply in early spring, and migration is in full swing.

FREEZE: GOODSHOOT / JUPITERIMAGES UNLIMITED; CONTAINERS, DIRT: BRAND X PICTURES; BIRDHOUSE, PRUNING: RDA·GID; ROBIN: ROLAND JORDAHL

summer

By now you're probably enjoying the fruits of your labor from spring planting. Your backyard may look amazing, but there's still plenty to do during the summer months.

- **HANG DIFFERENT-SIZED BIRDHOUSES** in a variety of habitats to attract the greatest numbers of nesting birds.

- **WATER EFFICIENTLY.** Invest in some soaker hoses, and snake them through your flower beds and vegetable patch before the plants get too large to navigate around.

- **PUT OUT GRAPE JELLY OR ORANGE MARMALADE** to attract birds such as orioles, gray catbirds, mockingbirds and red-bellied woodpeckers.

- **DON'T NEGLECT YOUR HANGING BASKETS!** They quickly dry out in warm summer weather, so check on them often and water generously.

- **FORGET RED-DYED SUGAR WATER**—it's no longer considered necessary for hummingbird feeders. Instead, look for a feeder with red on it and fill it with colorless sugar water. Or tie a red ribbon around your feeder.

- **START HARVESTING** cucumbers, peppers and summer squash. This practice encourages more production, plus you don't want them to rot on the vine. You can always donate surplus to neighbors or a local food bank.

- **FREQUENTLY REPLENISH BIRDBATH WATER** during hot, dry summer weather. Be sure to keep the depth to 2 inches or less in a birdbath so birds can stand while bathing.

- **KEEP AFTER WEEDS.** Yank them out by their roots. If you're pressed for time, snap off their flowers before they can go to seed. Many weeds spread by both means.

fall

The autumn season requires a lot of cleanup work. And for many regions in the U.S. and Canada, gearing up for the cold weather can be quite a task.

- **REMOVE ALL SUGAR-WATER FEEDERS** after the last orioles and hummingbirds have passed through the area.

- **SAFELY STORE FERTILIZER AND GARDEN CHEMICALS** in a secure location away from pets and children.

- **LEAVE SEVERAL BIRDHOUSES UP** all winter as roosting sites for chickadees, bluebirds and woodpeckers.

- **LET HEALTHY, PEST-FREE PERENNIALS STAND** for fall and into winter. They add beauty to the winter landscape, provide food for birds and are winter homes for many beneficial insects.

- **PICK TOMATOES THAT ARE STARTING TO SHOW COLOR** before the first killing frost, and ripen them indoors.

- **LOOK FOR FALL SWALLOWTAILS** in the East and Midwest, such as pipevine, black, spicebush and tiger.

- **STOP MUSHROOMS** that have sprouted in your yard—your best bet is to take a rake to them. Knock off their tops, and cart them away.

- **STOCK UP ON SUNFLOWER SEEDS IN ANY FORM.** They offer the greatest amount of energy for the birds of winter.

- **PLANT SMALL TREES,** such as flowering dogwood and redbud, to provide hosts for the spring azure and Henry's elfin butterflies. Also, plant shrubs in the autumn to offer extra cold-weather shelter for songbirds, and a perching spot for spring butterflies.

Hardiness Zones

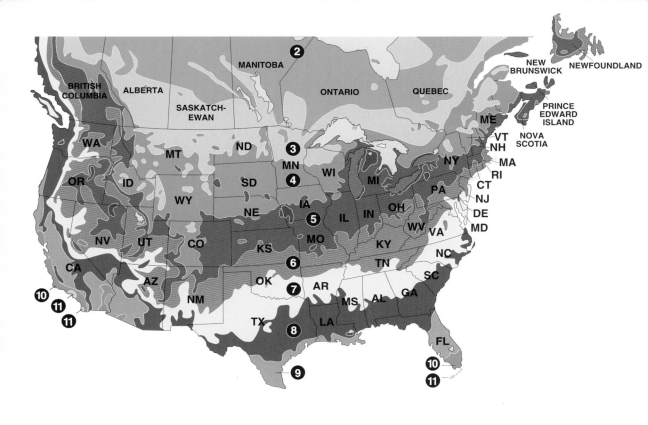

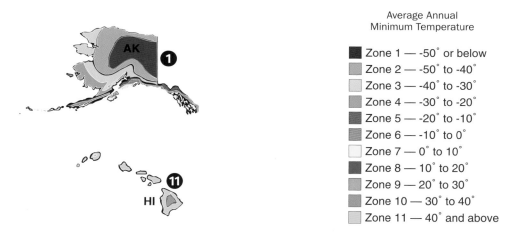

Average Annual
Minimum Temperature

- Zone 1 — -50° or below
- Zone 2 — -50° to -40°
- Zone 3 — -40° to -30°
- Zone 4 — -30° to -20°
- Zone 5 — -20° to -10°
- Zone 6 — -10° to 0°
- Zone 7 — 0° to 10°
- Zone 8 — 10° to 20°
- Zone 9 — 20° to 30°
- Zone 10 — 30° to 40°
- Zone 11 — 40° and above

Heat Zones

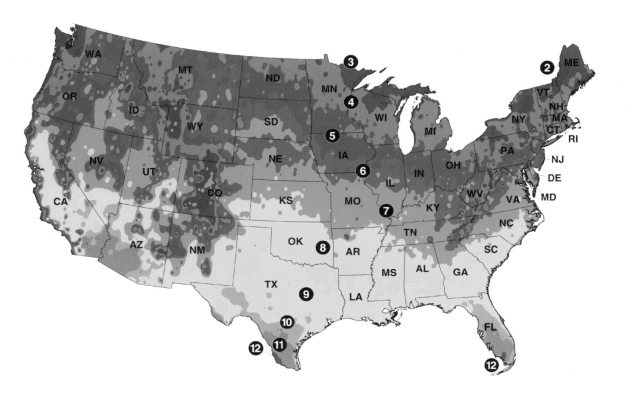

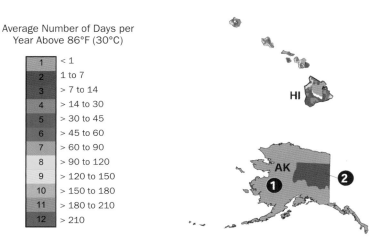

Average Number of Days per
Year Above 86°F (30°C)

1	< 1
2	1 to 7
3	> 7 to 14
4	> 14 to 30
5	> 30 to 45
6	> 45 to 60
7	> 60 to 90
8	> 90 to 120
9	> 120 to 150
10	> 150 to 180
11	> 180 to 210
12	> 210

Maps courtesy of the American Horticultural Society. The zones featured should be treated as general guidelines when selecting plants for your garden. For more information on your specific region, visit usna.usda.gov/Hardzone/ushzmap.html.

Notes